The Little Book Of Doggerel Story Verse And Play

By

Louie Byrne

Best Wishes

Louie Byrne

DEDICATED TO MARY SLATTERY
For Her
Tenacious Courage And Optimism In Face Of Remittent
Disappointments.
For Laughing In The Face Of Adversity And Pessimism.

First Edition (Limited) 2003 Copyright Louie Byrne.

Isbn 0 9524278 4 2

Now quench the lamp and hide our shame,
For this is not a childish game.
In famine fever I lay me down,
As stately ships from a foreign crown,
Laden with produce stolen from Celtic soil,
Obscenely pass as our children die.

Extract from Famine Fever. Louie Byrne. ©

I trust that you the reader may gain as much pleasure from reading this little book as I did writing it.

All characters in this publication are fictitious any resemblance to real persons, living or dead, is purely coincidental.

All rights reserved. No part of this publication may be reproduced stored in a retrial system or transmitted in any form whatsoever, or by any means, electronic, mechanical, photocopying, and recording or otherwise without the prior permission of the publishers.

Published by Premier Books
Unit 'R'
Cradock Road
Luton Lu4 OJF Bedfordshire
Tel: 01582572727/ FAX01582585868

Isbn 0 9524278 4 2

FORWARD

The island of Ireland has long been protected from the opinionated influence of the religions of Europe and elsewhere. Mytholipoetic culture has long been extinguished elsewhere but not so in Ireland. Ireland with its own culture and language and protected by the seas has retained a natural and inborn religious belief, half Christian and half Celtic.

One has only to visit her many wells and trees when seeking proof of this. These were sacred long before Christianity came to our shore and perhaps more so. Christianity did not change any of the old Celtic customs, i.e. placing the bandages, sticks and crutches of the sick on the sacred tree over the well in thanksgiving and atonement to their Gods.

Walking from East to West in bared feet 'round the well. Many of these old customs are observed to day as they were by the magic of a thousand, thousand years. Christianity adopted these wells and renamed them with the names of saints. Yet many to this day still retain their Celtic names. (Morning Star, Doon, Sionna, Hawthorn Mist. etc:)

The dead were held in high esteem in Ireland and more so in the South/West. No keening was permitted at a wake until three hours had passed after the death. The purpose of this was to allow the spirit of the dead to pass unhindered to the 'Astral' world from where it came at mortal birth. Any keening would arouse from slumber the two great hounds of Hades who wait in ambush at the gates of the underworld. Keening would also inhibit the spirit from giving an account of its stewardship on earth to the great God **LUG** lesser gods and princesses.

Irish keening with its long wailing cry of Úl-lú-lú-lú, has a strange mystical calling. One cannot listen to it but feel a strong emotion of love and gentle sorrow. It washes over you like cleansing waters, once heard it's not easily forgotten. Here as an example a distraught mother keens over the body of her dead son. Who now, she cries will there be to say the hungry prayers over her corpse when she is no more?

4

Mo Cúshla, look on me!
Look on me and see,
Have you ever known sorrow like mine?
The sorrow is mine on seeing you die.
Arran, mo brón, mo cushla:
Úl-lú-lú-ló-ló.
'Tis your mother that calls you, mo cúshla.
How long is your sleeping?
'Tis sore is my weeping.
Your people have gathered, allanah
Úl-lú-lú-ló-ló
The road is so fada, (Long)
There's paleness on your face.
No longer beauty, no longer grace;
The stranger will now take me to my grave
For you my child, they've taken away.
Úl-lú-lú-ló-ló.

Many of the stories I tell have been handed down through the mystical stories of Finvarra, who is king of all the fairies and his queen Ónagh.

One day as Finvarra and his queen Ónagh were walking through the beautiful glens and mountains of the lands of Tír-na-nÓg, they chanced upon Saint Columcille praying. Seeing them approaching he remembered that according to the teachings of the Church they were once angels in heaven. They had offended his God and for their punishment were cast down to earth. He knew that they retained great powers and beauty. They had the secret of eternal youth and a joy of music. Their great God 'LUG' bestowed this gift on them when they passed from the astral world to mortal life.

Why had not his God given him such great gifts? He thought. Though a great saint he was jealous of their wisdom and powers. Rising he approached them and instead of greeting them in friendship as is the Irish custom; he reproached them and made the following prediction...

'You will die without any hope of redemption, for sure as the human race is created immortal, so you are doomed to annihilation. There is no hope and no redemption for you. You will, on the day of judgement

5

pass from death to hellfire. This punishment was decreed and imposed on you and your race by God himself.' Like a poisoned chalice he spate out the curse with venom, unbecoming a great saint, at the King and queen. On hearing the curse Queen Ónagh was most distressed and fell into a profound melancholy.

Not so the king, for he was the king of all the fairies and very wise. He knew that it was jealously on the part of the saint that made him so spiteful. There was no such a punishment from their great God. Looking deep into the saints eyes he replied...

'Is there not but one God, our God and your God? I do not and could not speak for the great God nor should you. If all you say were true, and I know that it is not, then there would be no indulgence in us doing good deeds. Saint Columcille having been chastised by the fairy king went away to pray for forgiveness for his jealously and angry outburst. He never troubled the Sídhe race again.

The mythology found throughout Ireland reveals the relationship of her people to the spiritual mysterious and invisible world of Tír-na-nÓg. Stop and wonder at our ancient monuments, our Cromlechs, Dolmens, Mehirs and Tumuli. These are solemn and eternal symbols of our faith, the rituals of the stones, the pillars and temples. Powerful granite temples anchored to the very bowels of the earth and from there reaching up in strength to the skies. The language of our race is written in Ogham on her stone pillars in sacred knots and circles.

In my youth, story telling or Sean Scéals was as common in households as are televisions to day. There was no lack of a captive audience when the Seanachai (Story-Teller) took his/her seat beside the hob. Many of the stories I relate came from that time and place. There are few Seanachai to be found to day. Alas! These are now confined to the great banqueting halls and tourist attractions.

As your Seanachai I hope to preserve some of these stories and tales. I trust that they will be handed down to a new generation. There is still much therapeutic value to be found in the old Sean Scéals. Sit back, quench the light and riddle the fire. Put a spleen to your piopca. Wash your dreams in the mystic of an Irish night.

Wander through Tír-na-nÓg; the view of the five counties from haunted Knockfierna hill near to Ballingarry in the county Limerick is breathtaking. Fly to Lough Gur on gossamer wings. Benbulben, the

6

fairies playground and the hills of Donegal are not that far away in fancy dreams. You pass the Costa Bower without fear...

Shure why am I telling you all this? Come in from the cold of the night and a Céad Míle Fáilte to your good self. Take the weight off your feet and the stone from your heart. Close your eyes and listen. Listen mo cúisla to the singing in the chimney. Is it the wind or the call of the Tuatan de Dannan? More likely is it the shriek of the Bean-Ó-Sidhe...Dream? Dream on and on.

THE CELTIC WARRIOR

He is gone! He is gone, they cried in sorrow,
What's left for us to day, to morrow?
We'll keep his memory in fallowed fields,
As o'er his grave grows the Ivy Green.

Then in this place we laid him down,
In Ogham stone his name renowned.
They let him rest in Celtic dreams,
As slowly grew the Ivy Green.

Where is that dream? Alas forgotten,
The Ogham stone now slowly rotting.
What of his sacrifice, what did it mean?
His accolade lost in the Ivy Green.

Yet we who loved and served you well,
Cherish your deeds to write and tell.
No trumpet sound to disturb your sleep;
Gossamer silk spun on ivy Green.

Who now is there to speak your name?
Your sacrifice; was it all in vain?
Sleep on brave knight in Celtic dreams,
As o'er your grave grows the Ivy Green.

LOUIE BYRNE©

8

The Maligned Faithful Companion

In the county of Limerick There's a town named Bruree,
Twas there lived a dog, named Scamp you see.
No love had his master for that old shaggy dog.
A cruel blast from his twin bore finally silenced his call.'

I have little doubt but there are those who will greet my tales with
some incredulity. I ask in all sincerity 'Would I lie to you?'
You may have passed through the old village of Bruree in your time
and wondered why a memorial to a hound was erected in the village?
Wonder no more, for I will tell you the Sean Scéal here and now...

It was glorious morning in late September in the year 1843. The
village of Bruree in County Limerick was bracing itself for a fine
harvest. Mother and the eldest daughter had been up and about for
some time preparing food. This was the day of the reaping, known as
'The Harvest fair.' The sun had burnt the morning dew from the ripe
crop. The neighbours were gathered under the roof to participate in a
hearty breakfast in preparation of a good days work.
The old hound, a faithful companion of the family for fifteen years sat
beside the cradle in which lay the newborn son of the family named
David. The old dog, named 'Scamp' for no apparent reason had taken
to the child as a bitch would take to her litter. There was little doubt
but that he was over protective to the child. Should a stranger
approach the cradle or for that matter look sideways at it, and then he
was up on his feet, showing his teeth and growling
"Lie down Scamp, sure nobody is going to steal David." These words
were enough to assure the dog that all was well. Yet he still kept a
wary eye for any suspicious movements.
"There is little need for you to worry for your son, Mary. Not as long
as you have Scamp on guard." Would come the complimentary
remarks With the breakfast consumed the gathering collected their
reaping hooks and scythe and went into the fields. Mary, the woman of
the house remained behind and tidied up the kitchen before she too
prepared to go to the meadow and make the hay ropes to bind the

9

stacks. Mary looked over at the old dog sitting beside the cradle before she too left the house.

"Now Scamp, I have to be down the fields, I want you to keep watch over David. Do you hear me?" The old dog gave her a knowing look and wagging his tail moved even closer to the cradle, if that were possible.

"There is little fear for my child when I have you my madra dílis (faithful dog)." She looked kindly towards the old dog before going and patting him on the head. Scamp stood up and with an appreciative look once again wagged his tail. He too liked to be complimented and not to be taken for granted. In by gone days he would have been down the field chasing any disturbed rabbits during the cutting. This was no longer possible, for now he was crippled with pains and half blind. He contented himself with the warmth of the kitchen fire and guarding the infant. He had a duty to perform and he would not be found wanting. The work in the field continued well into the day. Midday came and it was decided that they would stop for a well-earned meal and a rest...

It is here that the story takes a twist that is difficult to comprehend. Perhaps there are others who have a different version of the event of that day. Here however is the truth of what was related to me around the old turf fire so very long ago. Pat, the husband held a terrible secret resentment against the old dog. It all happened, or so it seemed, on the day that Scamp came to the house as a pup. Scamp took a craving to Mary the master's wife and became her constant companion. The husband's malevolence for the dog had been simmering for all those years. Leaving the fields that day he returned to the house. He looked down at the faithful dog guarding the cradle. As he passed he raised his studded boot and gave the poor old dog a kick. Scamp let out a low moan and with tears in his eyes retreated to safety. Ignoring the dogs suffering he entered the scullery where he took a long drink of sweet milk from the churn. Returning to the kitchen he sat down and studied the old dog. The dog in turn looked up at his master and slowly wagged his tail. Strange it was that they never really did trust each other. There was a kind of love hate relationship between them. It was with hatred in his eyes that the master decided there and then to kill the old dog. Taking his gun down from over the mantle he approached the cradle. The dog had a premonition that something was wrong and crawled nearer to the

10

cradle, determined on defending David. Little did he know that it was his life that was in impending danger? Loading the gun, his master raised it to his shoulder and pointing it at the old dog fired. Blood from the animal spattered the linen of the cradle. The old dog let out a sorrowful howl and fell on his side. David began to cry alerting the old dying dog. In a final effort to protect the infant he crawled towards the cradle. He let out a mournful sigh before he fell dead, trying to defend his charge. This cruel and final act was the culmination of the farmers pent up hatred for an innocent and devoted animal.

Removing the infant from the cradle, Pat tipped it over and ran from the cottage calling for help. He told the neighbours that when he returned to the cottage he found the cradle overturned and the dog foaming at the mouth about to attack his son. He had no alternative but to shoot him in defence of his child. Whatever credence there was in his story they had little alternative but to accept his explanation. There was no logical reason as to why anyone would want to kill faithful old Scamp.

It was some time after the incident that the master took to wandering and chasing something away from beside him. The neighbours soon noticed his strange behaviour; they were of the opinion that he was losing his mind. Unable to stand the tension he approached his wife and confessed to his cruel deed.

"It's his ghost that keeps following me. I pray to Jesus for him to go away and leave me in peace. I'm going insane. Mary please help me?" Little peace did he get neither day nor night and finally took to his bed. The doctors could find no physical malady wrong with him. One morning as his wife came to his bedside with a bowl of nourishing gruel he saw the ghost of old Scamp trotting beside her. The dog stopped at the bedside as with tear filled eyes looked up at him and wagged his tail. 'Was he asking forgiveness for failing in his duty, or was he asking his master to confess to the truth'? We'll never know. Pushing the bowl to one side Pat sat up in the bed and called his wife to him.

"Mary! Mary, please ask him to forgive me? It's old Scamp he will never rest until I confess to the truth." Pat held his hands before his face and pleaded. There and then he confessed to his jealously of the dog. He told her how he had killed faithful old Scamp. He begged her to forgive him. He pleaded with the apparition to give him peace.

"I cannot bring you back from the dead Scamp; I can only restore your good name. In God's holy name, please Scamp I beg of you; give me peace?" Pat held his hand out to the ghost. The spectre remained behind the safety of his wife staring at him and wagging his tail.

"Will you forgive me, will you please show me mercy?" He again in desperation pleaded with the ghost of the old dog still looking at him wagging his tail.

"Will who forgive you?" Mary asked, a puzzled look on her face.

"Scamp, that's who, he is standing beside you. Don't you see him?" Pat stammered.

"Scamp forgives you as we all do, don't you Scamp?" Mary looked down at the floor. She could sense a presence; but saw nothing. Then she felt the cold nose nudge her hand.

"We will never forget you Scamp, have no fear." Tears came to her eyes as she felt the ghostly presence of the old dog. Soon after making his confession Pat recovered. The old dog was never seen again in the house. He had been exonerated by the confession of Pat, his master.

The body of Scamp was recovered from the dung heap where it had been ignominiously thrown. He was buried beneath an ancient Celtic stone beside the sweet water well. A resting place, you'll no doubt agree befitting a noble and gentle friend.

Mary, long into her years still heard him bark his greeting as she went to the fairy well to collect water. "It's only me, Scamp old friend." She would remind the ghost, as she hobbled with the aid of her stick up the well-worn boréen with her bucket of sweet water. His spirit was still guarding the old homestead. Mary and all belonging to her have since passed from life to mortal dream. May Heaven open up its gates to them, one and all? The old house fell into decay many, many years ago. Scamp! Well he still guards the old homestead or what remains of it.To day there is a sculpture of a faithful old dog sitting on a well-worn carraig (Rock) in the town of Bruree. Mary had it erected before she too passed into the long sleep of a Celtic night.

That dog is Scamp, the dog who refused to die.

'They laid him down in Celtic sleep,
They did not sigh, nor did they weep.
'Neath Ogham stone they let him rest,
Sleep on old pal, you were the best.'

12

THE GHOSTS OF OULD LIMERICKS' KILKEE

'Tis many years since mother took me by the hand,
From our humble room in the workhouse on Clancy Strand.
A trip to the seaside was to us but a dream,
As we paddles our feet in Shannon streams:
The ould West Clare, passed by us and screeched
On it's way to the seaside far from Limerick's Kilkee.

The ladies lake still sits in Shannon's crystal pool,
'Twas where we swam and fished and leisure took;
As mother watched o'er us and read her beads,
In her sad, sad eyes, we read her tears.
As the golden sun- set, o'er Ould Shannon's Quay's.
She thanked her God for Ould Limerick's Kilkee.

On a wooden seat she'd take her ease,
Then tell us tales of the Ould Bean-Ó-Sidhe:
As the Limerick boat club eight rowed out,
We'd jump on the seats and wave about.
There she'd open a bottle of sweetened tea,
Shure we'd take our ease on Ould Limerick's Kilkee

In foreign climes where we were forced to roam,
Mothers last wish was to be taken home.
The night she died I closed her eyes,
And I promised to lay her beside Shannon side.
She held my hand and smile did she,
Then I heard her Bean-Ó-Sidhe cry past Limerick's Kilkee.

I retraced my steps the other day,
To reminisce on the past and to say a prayer:
But the Shannon tide had been diverted,
From childhood dreams I was converted.
As with a gentle chiding a foreman stopped me,
From taking my rest in Ould Limericks Kilkee.

Most of the old folk are all but forgotten
The Ould wooden seats have long since rotted.
Now mother's ghost can no longer stay,
For the green sward they've taken away.
She now wanders the waters with her Bean-Ó-Sidhe.
For there's no longer a welcome in Ould Limerick's Kilkee.

God be with the folk from Shannon side,
And Martin McGuire's near Curragower:
Alas! The Ould swivel bridge is silent now.
Shure the mills now gone from Francis Street,
As have the folk from Arthur's Quay.
For no longer the turf boats pass Ould Limerick's Kilkee.

A marina will stand where I fished and swam,
Where the folk of Limerick sat, they've built a dam.
Yet the ghosts of yesterdays will roam, I pray,
Between the marina and Honan's Quay,
We'll meet one day, you and me,
Shure we'll have the 'Craic' in Ould Limerick's Kilkee.

You've **'Rippled my Pond'** I dare to say,
For the better of Limerick, I know some day:
Now why did you ruin it, my lovely stand?
I crave your indulgence for I don't understand,
Why you filled in my strand beside the quay,
And banished forever Ould Limerick's Kilkee.

I turned on my heel and walked away,
Yet my lady's pond still there, I'm glad to say.
My mother's ghost still guards my path,
Past the old fort and fairy rath.
Where Shannon waters flowed fast and free,
Past Sarsfield bridge to Ould Limerick's Kilkee.

©LOUIE BYRNE

14

THE HEADLESS COACH

'Why the hearse with 'Scutcheons' blazoned round,
And with the nodding plume of Ostrich crow'nd?
No! The dead know it not, nor profit gain.
It only serves to prove the living vain.
How short is life! How frail is human trust!
Is all this pomp for laying dust to dust?'

There are several stories told relating to the Coste Bower, the most famous I related to in **'Dare You Ripple My Pond'**. Read slowly and ponder as I relate another encounter with the **Death Coach...**

Lady Bowden-Jones, the honourable wife of Sir William Bowden-Jones of Shannon Manor, Foynes in County Limerick, sat by the bedside of her seriously ill husband, holding his hand. Listening to his heavy breathing she numbered her beads and prayed for his speedy recovery. Downstairs the servants went silently about their duties. Mary, her faithful and long standing servant silently left the kitchen and closed the door behind her. Standing at the foot of the wide ornate staircase, she paused. Then placing her hand on the balustrade she crept up the stairs. Approaching the door of her master's bedroom she knocked gently.
"Yes! Who is it?" The mistress called interrupting her prayers.
"Is there anything that we can do, mam?" The servant asked discretely from the other side of the closed door.
"Nothing Mary, thanks! He is in Gods hands, we can but wait and pray." Came the sorrowful reply.
'Caesar' Their Irish wolf hound and faithful companion of the master lay unobtrusively under the bed. He knew that all was not well with his master. No longer did they roam the grounds of the vast estate, as was their daily routine. He now remained on guard beside his master's bed. At the slightest movement he would raise his big shaggy head and wag his tail in anticipation. When his master did not respond he would look with pleading sorrowful eyes at the still form lying in the bed. Then with a sigh, rest his head between his great paws. It was as if he knew that the sands of time were slowly running out for his master.

Mary paused before the closed door for a moment. Uttering a sigh she silently left her mistress to her sorrow. There was little that could be done. The master's life was now in the hands of the Almighty God. Creeping down the stairs she studied the large oil paintings of generations past. Each past member of the family sat in their large gilded frames dressed in their finest robes. The honours presented to them by past kings and queens proudly displayed in the appropriate place on their attire for all to see and admire. Many defiantly sat on their chargers dressed in defensive suits of armour.

As the light of the candle illuminated each portrait, it came apparent that they were watching and waiting. Another painting would soon fill another space on the wall. Mary retreated down the last few steps of the great staircase and entered the servant's quarters. At the door leading into the kitchen she was relieved to hear the chatter of the other servants. As she opened the door, the assembly fell silent and glanced towards her with questioning eyes. Shaking her head she sat down on the nearest chair. Releasing her pent up emotions, then with a heavy heart she wept openly and unashamedly.

"The mistress has sat up there for the last week hoping and praying for a miracle?" She sighed between her weeping. She had always been a good and faithful servant. The family held her in high esteem.

"Sure, don't we all know that it is only a matter of time? God be good to his soul. Here drink your tea, you have been a God send to the mistress in her sorrow." Came the sympathetic response as Bridget, the fat jovial cook gently pushed a china cup towards Mary.

"Don't reproach yourself Mary, as cook says you have been a bastion of strength to us all at this tragic time." The butler laid a friendly hand on her shoulder. Mary came to the great house at the tender age of ten years. Her parents had died when she was still an infant. She found herself incarcerated in an orphanage in the city. It was there that her ladyship found her and took her to her manor. Over the years a strong bond developed between mistress and servant.

Upstairs the mistress continued to speak in whispers to her husband. It was as if she were trying to cram a lifetime into their last hours together. She knew that it was only a matter of time before his departure from this life. Yet in some recess of her mind she refused to accept the inevitable.

16

It was some two nights later that the mistress called urgently for Mary to come to the bedroom. Lighting a candle and placing it in its holder she went up the long staircase and across the hall. Transferring the candleholder to her left hand she knocked delicately on the oak door and turning the brass handle entered the room. Caesar; on hearing her enter lifted his head and wagging his tail looked with pleading eyes towards her. Calling him to her side she stroked his head and comforted him. Seeing the sadness in the eyes of the old dog a lump came into her throat. Sobbing gently she wiped away her tears. The flickering light from the candle penetrated the darkness and danced along the heavy drapes and canopy of the large four-posted bed. Atop each post a fierce looking gargoyle stood guard and looked down on her questioning her intrusion. She took little notice of them in the past. Now they were intimidating her.

"Go away, you have no right to be here." They screamed.

Moving the candle closer to the bed she hesitated and looked up at a fierce looking dragon studying her with fire in his eyes. She could hear the heavy intermitting breathing of her master within the confines of its velvet folds, she knew that he was fighting for his life.

"It's alright Mary, you can come closer." Her mistress interrupted her dreaming as she looked from around the confines of the drapes.

Mary noticed that she held her rosary firmly in her hands. It seemed that although she knew there was now no hope, she was reluctant to accept it. She returned to the bedside and closed the drapes. Apart from the dim flickering of the candle the room was in darkness. Yet she did not wish to intrude. She felt embarrassed, as if she were spying on the intimate affairs of two lovers.

"Mary would you ever light the gas mantles. I was not aware that it was so late?" She drew back startled as the voice of her mistress again penetrated her dreaming. Crossing to the fireplace, where two brass gaslights in ornate cut glass globes were screwed to the wall, one each side of the over mantel. Reaching up she turned the tap on the first lamp; there was a hissing sound of escaping gas. Holding her candle near to the mantle she heard the 'pop' as it ignited. On the far wall ghostly shadows followed her every movement. Nervously she glanced at the unobtrusive shadows and repeated the operation with the second mantle.

"That is better, thank you Mary." The room now lit with the incandescent light from the two gaslights no longer intimidated her. The four-poster bed threw a long flickering shadow across the room. Mary had never noticed this before.

"Would Madam care for a bowl of broth? Taking the liberty Mam, you have not eaten this day." Mary stood with the candleholder secure in her hand.

"Thanks Mary, you are a God send. I don't know how I would have managed without you."

"How is the master, if I may be so bold as to ask?" Ignoring the compliment she asked.

"The master Mary; is very, very ill, we must prepare for the worst."

"It's sorry we are to hear this mam. Is there no hope at all?" Mary spoke for all the servants.

Like an actress about to accept an accolade her ladyship came from behind the drapes. Holding tightly to the silken cord holding the heavy curtain she looked towards Mary. Then shaking her head and raising her hands she retreated once again behind the confines of their folds. Mary felt her blood rushing through her ears as a deadly silence filled the room. That was apart from the heavy breathing of the master.

The old dog let out a sigh and rested his head between his paws.

She paused for a moment unsure as to what to do next before genuflecting and quietly leaving the room.

Soon she returned with a tray on which sat a bowl of steaming hot broth and a plate of daintily sliced home baked scone.

The jolly fat cook had hoped that the delicate meal would tempt her ladyship into eating. She laid the tray on the side table and left the room without saying a word. Her mistress was now in deep conversation with her dying husband. This was an intimate conversation, a secret not to be shared.

Mary retired to her bedroom and kneeling at the side of her bed she prayed. She prayed for the repose of her master's soul. She also prayed for relief for her mistress. Rising to her feet she raised the bedclothes and removed the stone hot water jar. With a final prayer she lay down and soon succumbed to sleep. The chores in a large mansion were arduous and the hours long. More especially now that the master was so ill.

She was awakened by the sound of a coach being driven at high speed up the drive. Curiosity getting the better of her she rose from her bed. She was about to draw the drapes to see who was calling when a foreboding came over her. She stood transfixed before the closed drapes. She knew instinctively who the callers were and why they were calling this night. Falling to her knees she withdrew her rosary from under her pillow and began to pray. There was something not right this night. She could hear the coach being driven at great speed backwards and forwards. Terror of the night gripped her as she listened and tried to pray, but the coach did not stop. She heard too the Dullahán cracking his whip noisily. There was great agitation outside. They were impatient to be on their way with their passenger.

She knew it was the Coiste Nior Ceann Luga. She knew also that she dared not draw the drapes and look. The Dullahán would see her and flick out her eyes with a swish from his long whip.

She heard the great socraid (procession) as it walked briskly up and down the drive. They were waiting and chanting, waiting impatiently for the inevitable.

Mary now petrified with fear and foreboding slowly rose to her feet and stood transfixed before the drapes. She knew why they had come calling. She wished them a thousand miles away. She longed to rush to the side of her mistress and comfort her. If only they would go away and leave them to their sorrow.

"Stop! Go away, Please God send them away." She held her hands to her ears and pleaded.

Yet she knew in her heart that they would soon be going away but not with an empty coach. The Coiste Nior Ceann Luga never left without its passenger.

She heard the grandfather clock in the great hall strike the hour of midnight. She began to count each chime as it vibrated around the house.

She clasped her hands tightly over her ears endeavoring to deafen the chimes. But they would not be silenced; they continued their mournful dirge.

The chimes did not stop at the midnight hour. It struck one extra note, a death knell out of respect for her late master.

19

As the chimes died away into the walls of the mansion she heard a great scuffling. It was the horses from the Coiste Nior Ceann Luga scraping the ground impatiently. Of this she was convinced. There were also noises and keening of a great impatience within and without the great house. She would not look nor dared she.

"Go away! Go away in Gods holy name." She again pleaded.

In the distance she heard the servant bell being rung urgently. Duty bound she forced herself to leave her room and go down the hall to the master bedroom. Beside the bed her mistress clinging to the last vestige of hope was crying bitterly as she cradled her dying husband.

"He's dying Mary, did you hear them?" Mary did not reply but went to the side of the bed. She encouraged her mistress to kneel beside her for the final act of contrition. Rising she took the liberty of putting her arms round her and assisting her to her feet. The old dog crawled closer to the head of the bed and began to moan. Slowly he rose to his feet and coming to the bedside placed a great paw in the hand of his dying master as if in a final farewell. Then moving closer he lifted his head and licked his masters hand. With a final sigh of resignation he removed his paw and walking slowly to the door lay down "It is time Mam, you done all you could. Let him go now, please." Mary taking a liberty removed her mistress's arms from around her husband and cradled her in her own. He had others callers now, they would not be discouraged. She heard the neighing of the insistent horses and knew what she had to do. "Please do not touch him Madam." She knew that his spirit was now transcendent and anxious to leave. Rising to her feet she took the liberty of opening the bedroom door. The spirit of the master was now free to take his seat in the <u>Costa Nior Bower.</u> They heard the cracking of the great whip and the sound of a moving coach. They saw the light from the gas mantles glow dim; they knew that the final act was about to be played. It came, as they knew it would. The mournful dirge from the riverbank followed by an urgent knocking on the bedroom door. The Bean-Ó-Sidhe and the Buacaillíní Miocumta (deformed boy) were doing the final calling. The old dog rose to his feet and joined in the keening. Then all fell silent and an unforeseen coldness entered the room. Three knocks were rapped on the great door.

Her ladyship was about to rise to her feet to answer the urgent knocking when Mary gentle restrained her.

"Please don't answer the door, Mam." She whispered.

"Why not Mary?"

"It's the master Mam! His spirit is fearful of travelling into the unknown. Whoever answers the door will be the next to die. With due respect Mam; the dead never like to go to the other world alone. He's seeking company." She warned.

They saw the light from the gas mantle grow dim and they knew that the final act was about to be played. Mary returned to the room and covered the mirrors. Going to the mantelpiece, she opened the glass face of the clock and taking hold of the pendulum stopped its movement. Returning to the deathbed she picked up the brown Connáil na Marb (Candle of the dead) and held it over the face of her dead master. She held the light close to his open eyes so his spirit could see the guiding light. Finally she closed them to the world of mortals for the last time. She waited as his mouth fell open, thus allowing his spirit to escape its earthly body. Gentle she closed his mouth. Her master's spirit was now free in the room and seeking guidance to the world beyond the grave. Using the flickering light as a guide she crossed the floor and opened the bedroom door wide. She genuflected out of respect as the spirit of her late master prepared to leave the house for the last time. She encouraged his spirit to follow the light from the world of his birth to the world of the dead. She felt the presence as his spirit followed the light down the great staircase. She was no longer afraid. There was a strange stillness about the portraits, as if a serene tranquillity had overcome them. Opening the great door to her master for the last time she held the Connáil Na Marb high and again genuflected.They heard the carriage door open and close. They heard the cracking of the great whip and finally the sound of a moving coach.

On the gravel drive Mary stood and waited, then a gentle zephyr quenched her candle.

The reluctant spirit of Sir William Bowden-Jones left Foynes in the County Limerick on the final journey.

THE OLD FRANCISCANS

Feeling nostalgic, my old city to see,
I packed up my case and crossed the Irish Sea:
The city looked grand, better I recalled,
Than when I **rippled the pond** near Curragower falls.
And the Angelus bell still calls us to prayers,
As the mighty great Shannon it echoes her praise.
Yet all of its callings now fall on deaf ears,
As rushing and fro in, too busy are we.
I was passing last week down old Henry Street,
Where as a youth the Franciscans, I'd humbly greet.
They've a quaint old church that to memory brings,
Reminder of times when their church bell did ring.
And the Angelus bell etc:
I smiled and remembered their blessings of yore,
As I reached up to open the door, now covered in mould.
I palmed its old timbers with a tear in my eye,
Perhaps I'm nostalgic, do you wonder why?
And the Angelus bell etc:
'Twas there my late mother did plead as she prayed,
To Blessed Saint Anthony to brighten her day.
But the door was shut tight, no way to get in,
My prayers and petitions were as well in the bin.
And the Angelus bell etc:
Pinned to the old door was a notice that read,
'No masses in this church, no petitions to be said.'
My eyes they were dimmed, my heart it was sore,
'Till the silence confirmed it, the church was no more.
And the Angelus bell etc:
" What's happened, please tell me, where have they all gone?
The friars and choristers that once chanted in song?"
Frustrated I called out but all was in vain,
There was no one to answer, no entry to gain.

LOUIE BYRNE©

(Dare you Ripple My Pond.)
Music by MARTIN TOURISH
(Stranolar County Donegal)

22

THE MONKS OF CLONMACNOISE

THE ABSENTEE

'He was never home when I called on him,
As hungry and cold I was want to sin.
Where could he be? Was he avoiding me?
What was my crime? Why boycott me?
The world he made in seven days,
Or so the Holy bible says.
I've waited for him for sixty years,
With supplicants and pleading tears.
I know he's there, I can feel his breath,
I know we'll meet at my hour of death.'

LOUIE BYRNE

Were not the monks of Clonmacnoise wise? Was it not they that wrote down the Táin Bó Cuailnge? My next story goes back in time long before a foreign force tried unsuccessfully, I'm glad to say, to destroy our race and our culture. When the only enemy were the elements of a harsh and barren land...

The monks of Clonmacnoise, mainly Cistercian and Augustinian monks claimed to be the wisest scholars in the whole of Ireland. Pride was not in keeping with the teaching of the holy mother church. They were supposed to be modest and humble.

However they were badly in need of funds and were searching for scholars to teach. They knew that there were many scholars in the land seeking learning and were willing to pay for it. They also knew that there were several other monks bent on the same task. I suppose one could say that it was a form of commerce on their part.

Now, it so happened that their greatest rivals had a monastery outside Mungret village in the county of Limerick. They too were renowned throughout the land for their knowledge and piety. So well they should be. Were they not taught by the great Saint Patrick and St Brendan themselves? These were modest monks and were not wise to the ways of the world. They kept themselves much to themselves.

The monks from Clonmacnoise decided that they would take the rocky road to Limerick. There they would openly challenge the monks of

Mungret to a public debate in Greek, Latin, Irish and French. Whichever order won the day would have the pick of the students.

When the monks from Limerick heard that the monks from Clonmacnoise were coming across the Shannon River to challenge them they were most disturbed. They had heard of the boasts of the other monks and no doubt believed all that they had heard. What were they to do? They would be humiliated in public by the great orators from Clonmacnoise. Something had to be done and quickly, for they were now on their way and would soon be knocking on the gates of the city. They assembled in their oratory one evening and began to pray for guidance from above. As they prayed they heard the great bell at the gate ring out. Pausing in the middle of their prayers they listened. Sure enough someone was ringing the bell. Perhaps they wanted a mass said for a departed soul. On the other hand they may be looking for alms. The abbot instructed one of the monks to go and see who was outside.

Returning he told the abbot that it was no more than a Bean-Ó-Botar (Woman of the roads) seeking a morsel of food? Now it was unknown for anyone to refuse hospitality to a beggar and so the abbot went to the kitchen and procured a small hamper. This he wrapped in a cloth and went to the gate. There he saw the woman covered in a heavy shawl.

"God bless your reverence and may heaven open its gates to you and all your brothers." She reached out for the parcel of food.

"God bless you my daughter and thank you." The abbot replied and making the sign of the cross over the woman, he blessed her. He looked down the road after the Sean bean boct an botar. He found peace and contentment within himself. Had he not gained an indulgence for his community by his charitable work that evening? Then as if God himself had answered their prayers in return he smiled and watched the old woman hobble down the boreén. Locking the gate he ran to the oratory. There was a smile on his face that would do credit to a Kilkenny cat.

"Brothers! The good Lord has heard our prayers." He panted as making the sign of the cross he looked up at the large crucifix of Christ hanging on the bare stonewall.

"What ails you brother Abbot, did someone attack you?"

24

"It's a miracle! A miracle I tell you brothers, praise be to the Lord."
Again he looked up at the cross and called on his fellow brethren to
join him in a humble prayer of thanks. Obediently and humbly they
knelt on the stony ground and prayed their thanks. What they were
thanking God for they did not know. Yet the brother abbot told them to
do so and he must be obeyed.

"There was nobody at the gate but a poor woman of the road. You told
us so yourself." The puzzled brothers reminded him on finishing their
prayers.

"A poor woman of the road she might be, but God has spoken to me
through her appearance this night. We will not be humiliated by the
monks from Clonmacnoise, you wait and see." Raising his hands to
the heavens he called on his brothers to give thanks once again. There
and then he disclosed his cunning plan. It is doubtful if such a devious
plot came from divine providence.

The following night the monks from Clonmacnoise arrived outside the
gates of the city of Limerick. The night being as dark as a raven's
wing. They were at a loss as to know which road to take to the abbey
at Mungret. Coming down the road they perceived a gathering of
women in black shawls. The Abbot called to them but they ignored him
and moved on. Raising his crosier he ran after them and stopped them.
"Do you know the road to the abbey at Mungret?" He asked.

One of the women came close to him and began to tell him how to get
there in Latin. The abbot and his brothers looked open mouthed at the
old crones. Then a second one interrupted the first and began to give
directions in French. She pointed to a narrow dirt road to their left. A
third old crone pushed the second to one side and raising her stick
began to give directions in Greek. The monks were flabbergasted by
the knowledge of these old women. It was not over yet, for a fourth
woman hobbled towards him and began to correct the third woman in
fluent Gaelic. As I said these were learned monks and began to
converse among themselves. They were confounded to hear such
eloquence coming from the mouths of what they considered to be
simple and ignorant women. The women not to be outdone soon joined
in the conversation. It mattered little what language the monks
addressed each other in. The women understood what they were
saying and replied in the same language. Finally the monks withdrew
to the safety of the city walls and out of earshot of the women.

25

"There is little use in us going to challenge the monks of the abbey at Mungret." The abbot superior told them as he rested wearily on his crosier.

"Why is that brother Abbot?" They questioned.

"If the women of Limerick are so conversed in the languages of the world and are so well educated, what knowledge must the monks of Mungret possess, dare we ask?"

"What should we do then, surely we cannot abandon our task?"

"We will return to our abbey at Clonmacnoise and never trouble the monks of Limerick again. We must never disclose that we ever came to Limerick, do you understand?" The Abbot general warned them.

With that they blessed the old women and bid them a very good night. They watched as the monks passed out of the city and on into Clare. The women saw them out of sight before removing their shawls.

"That was a good nights work brothers. I doubt if we will ever be bothered by the monks of Clonmacnoise again." With that the monks of Mungret returned to their Abbey.

That night they sang the 'Gregorian Chant' as it never had been sung before.

'THERE ARE MORE THINGS IN HEAVEN AND EARTH'...

Spring In The Air

The birds that in summer their sweet notes did sing,
Have long since departed, to their memory we cling.
Deep in their burrows the wild life is sleeping,
As o'er the green fields the cold ice is creeping.

The trees too are resting in hamlet and wood,
We've wrapped up quite warm, as rightly we should.
The snows of the winter fall silent and deep,
Then into the rivers and gullies it seeps.

The earth is in darkness, all silent and still,
Diana the night sky with moonbeams will fill.
Robin and linnet with sweet notes will thrill,
When the cold of winter makes way for the spring.

The snows of the winter will melt in the spring,
The birds will return their sweet notes to sing.
The trees will be dressed in their mantle of green,
And life will awaken from cold winter dreams.

LOUIE BYRNE©

There Be Ghosts ©

I'll not see them ever more;
The folk that sat outside my door.
With chat and 'craic' those jovial hosts;
Are silent now, for they be ghosts.

Yet I can see them gliding past;
That babbling brook, that old ships mast:
The Bean-Ó-Sidhe wail, the silent coast;
They follow me, for they be ghosts.

As spiders webs in the morning dew,
Carnage waits, a feast for few.
As tear drops, that no one can boast;
My sorrow fills, for they be ghosts.

A falling leaf on a gentle breeze,
Too soon the tree denuded be.
I'll too grow old, my grief is gross,
Alone I weep, for they be ghosts.

No mortal calls to my old door,
Forsaken now, I'm left alone.
I hear my neighbours, my name toast,
Why speak of me as if I'm a ghost?

I see myself in mirror shattered,
The dreams I knew are dead and scattered.
The sands of time the hourglass holds,
I too must go, for I am a ghost.

LOUIE BYRNE©

28

HE WHO SUPS WITH THE DEVIL NEEDS A LONG SPOON

CALLING HOME
'*I stand beside the reaper grim, the hourglass in his hand,*
I see his scythe, the lowering sand.
I know my race is nearly run.
Yet dare the mortal rejoice and say,
You go, for I must stay?
Your zest for life will not delay,
You too the gap must fill some day.'
Calling Home Louie Byrne.

If you are of a nervous disposition then I suggest that you do not attempt to open this story. You have been warned...

There lived in Watergate in the city of Limerick one Pat Slattery. He was a malicious debaucher and feared neither God nor man. It was one night after a heavy bout of drinking and gambling that it happened, God between us and all harm...

Pat had spent the night with a woman of ill repute, leaving his good wife to fend for their family as best she could. He was a blackguard if ever there was one, God forgive me. The hour was late when he left her bed and began his journey home. Passing the old city walls at Watergate he turned into the old graveyard intending to take the shortest route home. The graveyard believed to be the second oldest in the city is situated on the north side of the milk market in the city, so it is. On a path inside the graveyard what did he see but a human skull? In his drunken bravado he took a kick at the skull sending it deep into the undergrowth.
"You are welcome to come and join me to morrow." He laughed as he invited the skull and left the graveyard.
The following night as usual he was away to partake in a game of cards and a heavy night of drinking and the comfort of a woman's bed should she be willing. On his way home he again entered the old graveyard. He was more than surprised I can tell you when he was accosted by a tall gentleman. The gentleman was attired in a costume of an age long gone and on his head he displayed a silk top hat.

29

"Who do you think you are? Get out of my way?" He was in an offensive temper and tried to deliver a vicious blow on the gentleman. He was shocked and surprised when his hand passed through him. "What are you, in God's holy name tell me?" His bravado left him as he shrank away from the spiorad, (Spirit) for that is what he had encountered. He soon sobered up and was now fearful of the dark stranger standing menacingly above him.

"I sir, am the gentleman that you invited to join your party." Boomed the tall stranger.

"Go away! Go away at once. This is not real I must be having a nightmare." He screamed.

"You are not dreaming, Pat Slattery, Look?" Removing his tall hat he pointed to a large bruising on his forehead.

"This cruel injury was inflicted on me, an innocent soul, last night by you. Now it is you who are invited to join my party."

"This cannot be happening to me, go away leave me in peace." A cold sweat appeared on his forehead. He tried to run but his feet were like lumps of lead.

"Little peace do you give to others, including the dead. Now you plead for peace for yourself." The speaker smelling of decay informed him.

"What is it you want of me, anyway?" The snivelling wretch pleaded.

"Change your ways, change your ways Pat Slattery or else... Come the feast of Samain (All Souls Night) we will meet at this spot again." With that warning the spirit vanished into the night.

Pat returned home and threw himself into bed where he slept a long restless sleep into the following afternoon. He remembered what took place the previous night but foolishly dismissed it as a nothing but a bad dream. Time passed and the incident with the spirit was forgotten as far as he was concerned.

The feast of Samain came and Pat was away with his cronies for another night of drinking, card playing and debauchery. It being all souls night it would have been better had he gone to church and said a few prayers for the repose of the souls of the dead. It was a good night for him; the cards had fallen in his favour. His pockets were filled with sovereigns and his belly with finest punch. In the crisp air be began to sing an old commallie as he staggered towards the old graveyard.

At the entrance he saw the gentleman waiting swinging an ebony cane.

"You have arrived then, Pat Slattery?" The spirit spoke.

"So I have, and I don't give a curse for you." Pat showing his drunken bravado tried to look into the face hidden under the tall hat.

"You did not heed my warning then? Come! Follow me Pat Slattery, I have something special for you." The spirit began to glide out of the graveyard. Pat had no choice but to follow for he had no control over his movements. *"Come here."* The spirit stopped at the gate and called on Pat to join him. *"This is for you Pat Slattery."* Opening his cloak he withdrew a brown Connail na Marab (Candle of the dead)

"What need have I for a candle?" Pat laughed.

"Take it Pat Slattery! Take it and remember when the candle is spent so will your life be spent." The spirit foretold.

Pat found that although he had not taken the candle it was now in his hand. As the spirit vanished into the night the candle lighted itself. Shocked he held it for some time not knowing what to do with it. Then blowing it out and without thinking he put it in the pocket of his coatamore and returned home.

Time passed and he had forgotten all about the candle and the ghost. He had more pressing matters to attend to, drinking debauchery and card playing. The candle lay deep in the pocket of his old coatamore throughout the summer and on into the autumn.

On the feast of Samain his wife was alone in the house fending as usual for her children as best she could. There was no fire in the grate and no food on the table. The sparse candle had burnt itself out and the room was in darkness. *"Perhaps there's a copper in Pat's old coatamore."* She thought to herself. Rising she removed his old coatamore from behind the door and returned to her stool. She searched through the pockets and in one she found the Connail na Marbh. She was puzzled as to what a candle for the dead was doing in his pocket? Happy to find a light with which to finish the patching she placed it in an old saucer and lit it.

"May God's light show mercy to all the poor holy souls this night." She prayed as she lit the candle.

Meanwhile far away in the city her wayward husband continued his drinking, card playing and debauchery.

Mary, his wife sat beside the cold hob putting the final patch on a tattered jacket for one of the children by the light of the flickering candle. From time to time she would hold her cold hands round the

31

candle seeking a little heat. The candle burnt slowly nearer and nearer to the base of the broken saucer.

Midnight came and passed, Pat continued gambling and drinking long into the night. As the dawn broke in the east he left the den of iniquity. He had lost all his money and was in a foul mood. He staggered towards the graveyard where once again the spirit was waiting.

"What is it now, I've just about had enough of you?" Pat swore and tried to pass.

"I've come for you Pat Slattery, where I am taking you to you will have no need of money."

Mary put the jacket to one side as the candle spluttered and died.

"God be good to all the dead this blessed Halloween." She prayed and blessing herself she retired to her cold bed.

As the candle fluttered and died so Pat Slattery collapsed at the feet of the spirit and drew his last mortal breath.

Had she not lit the candle...perhaps??? Who knows?

ÚNA OF LOUGH KEY (TRINITY ISLAND)

'My Úna of the shimmering golden hair,
Like the chalice of gold gracing the royal fare:
Like a wild Irish rose, kissed by the dew,
I would curse my God, damned my soul for you.

My Úna, let the cold winds toss your hair,
Your grave holds you now, so tender, so fair.
Your warm body was once my love, my dream,
Now decays like flotsam in a weed-choked stream.

I waited, my darling, in waters so cold,
I reached out my hand to touch your curls of gold:
I waited in the stream so cold and strong,
I waited and fretted till the dawn had gone.

I turned my back, in sorrow strayed,
I fretted and worried since you died that day.
Lost in my grief I knew my fate,
I cursed your father in unchaste hate.

They came and told me, how you cried;
At the break of day, my love you died.
On Trinity Island, I'll lay my head,
Your cold, cold grave our bridal bed.

Should you happen to pass by Trinity Island in the River Barrow stop and ponder on the double grave of Úna Mac Dermott and Tomás Costello? Their graves do not tell their love story nor speak of their tragic end...

Let me tell you the Sean Scéal and when I am about it ask you to say a prayer and make a wish. Not for Úna and Tomás but for yourself. It is said that whoever wishes for love and happiness kneeling by their

33

graveside will have their prayers answered. They had so little love in their short lives that they want others to enjoy theirs. This is a Sean Scéal of love and tragedy. A story that will bring a tear to your eye and tare at your heart strings...

*Ú*na Mac Dermott was the beautiful daughter of Chief Mac Dermott of the clan Mac Dermott. She was but sixteen years of age when she fell in love with a young man by the name of Tomás Costello.

Their love for each other would have to remain a secret between them. Tomás was but a labouring boy, whereas she was the daughter of a chieftain. Love however found a way as it surely does.

Unknown to the chieftain arrangements were made for them to meet at a clandestine rendezvous. They met at every opportunity and vowed never to be parted from each other.

Chief Mac Dermott had other plans for his beautiful daughter. When the time came for her betrothal she would be married to a member of his clan. There was no place for a commoner in his plans.

Were he to allow such an arrangement it would bring scorn and shame on the clan name. It would challenge his right to arrange marriages between other members of the clan.

It was at one of their clandestine meetings that her father came upon them.

"What is the meaning of this?" He demanded to know from his daughter.

"I love Tomás Costello and none other will I marry." She vowed as she stood defiantly between her father and her lover.

"You will never meet again, do you hear me. As for you Tomás Costello, I forbid you ever to trespass on Trinity Island. Should you disobey me then you will find but a watery grave." With this warning he ordered his daughter back to the estate. Then he ordered his servants to strip Tomás and tie him to the nearest tree. Jumping off his horse he inflicted twenty lashes with his whip on the bared back of his victim as a chastisement.

Úna was confined to her room on the second floor of the mansion. Her window over looked the river Barrow. Daily she stood sentinel at the casement watching and waiting for her Tomás.

One day as she looked sorrowful across the water she saw a figure standing in the deep water. She heard his voice calling to her. There

34

was no doubt in her mind that it was none other than her lover Tomás Costello.

"I cannot cross the deep water to you, mo cúisla, but I send you my undying love." He called opening his arms wide.

"I love you Tomás and I will die before I let our love wane." She promised in return crying through her tears.

Tomás kept his daily rendezvous come hail, rain or snow. Standing waist deep in the cold water he would renew his vows of undying love for his Úna. Her melodious voice would reply likewise.

Not all the waters of the river could wash away their undying love.

One day her father walking along the riverbank saw Tomás in the water and heard him vowing his perpetual love for his daughter.

"So you will not obey my instructions, Úna? Let him call and plead but you and he will never be united. Never! You will be confined to a room at the back of the mansion." With these harsh words he closed the casement window.

Tomás kept a constant vigil in the river pledging his undying love for Úna. Her casement remained closed. Whatever could have happened to his Úna? He thought.

She could hear his plaintiff calling but alas could not reply.

She pleaded with her father to let her at least speak to Tomás, but he would not hear of it. Faithfully Tomás continued to come to the river calling in vain to his love. One morning when the servant came to her room she found Úna dead by the closed casement. She had died of a broken heart.

Still Tomás came and called for her not knowing that she was no more. The voice of his Úna that could not be stilled in life had been quenched in death.

The workers on the estate took pity on Tomás as he held a daily vigil for his lover who was no more. They defied the wish of their master and went to the waters edge and told him that his Úna was dead and buried.

Her lonely grave was situated on Trinity Island. He could now relax his vigil for there was no further reason for his calling.

Tomás refused saying that the ghost of his Úna would still hear him. He would keep his vigil and his vow to her.

"My Úna will hear me, she will be waiting for me to call. In life we loved each other, in death we will be united." He predicted through his tears.

Nightly he braved the river Barrow and swam to the grave of his sweetheart. There, alone with his love he would lie weeping on her grave until the dawn.

"I loved you in life, mo cuisla and I love you in death." His sorrowful message carried deep into her lonely grave.

Summer gave way to autumn and still he swam the river to her graveside. Winter came and with it came ice and snow but this did not deter Tomás. Breaking the ice with his bared fists until his blood flowed he would make a channel to the island. There was no obstacle on God's earth or beyond that could deter him from visiting his Úna.

That Christmas night: Tomás came to the riverbank carrying a berried holly bough. It was his Christmas present for his Úna. Placing the bough around his neck he broke the ice and entered the fast flowing river. When he reached the centre channel the current was so strong that he was being carried down river.

"Úna my love the river is wild, I need you Úna. I need your strength my love." He cried, as he was swept downstream. Razor sharp ice cut deep into his flesh as time and time again he was dragged beneath the ice. He swallowed copious amounts of water and was slowly drowning.

Above the crashing ice and the roar of the river he heard her calling to him.

"Come to me Tomás. Come! Our love is greater than all the rivers of Ireland." He heard her calling from within her lonely grave on Trinity Island.

With renewed strength he managed to make the shore. Staggering up the bank he crawled to the graveside of his Úna.

"I told you I would never forget you my love, I brought you a berried wreath." He laid the wreath at the head of the grave.

"I love you mo cuisla, I love you with all my heart. Soon we will be reunited." He stroked the headstone as he did her golden hair in life.

The moon cast her icy shadow on the lonely grave as the frost glistened on his slowly freezing shivering body.

Oblivious of the cold slowly sapping his lifeblood he made a pillow of the snow covering her grave.

"Úna mo cuisla, No longer will I need to swim the River Barrow to be with you." Over the ice covered river he heard the church bells ring out the Christmas message. Their obloquy lasted but a moment as his thoughts returned to his beloved sweetheart.

He tried unsuccessfully to rise from her lonely grave but could not.

"It is foreordained that we remain together. Weep no more gra geal mo croide." Raising his hand he scrolled his name in his blood next to hers on the freezing headstone. He continued speaking to his Úna as slowly and surely he surrendered his mortal life.

Next morning he was found covered in fresh snow, his hand frozen to the headstone. He was at last united with his Úna. He would never again need to swim the river Barrow to be with his childhood sweetheart.

When the old chief was informed of what happened on that faithful night his heart relented.

"Where should we bury the body of Tomás Costello?" They asked.

"Bury him beside his Úna, in life I denied them love. Forgive a selfish, bigoted old man." He openly wept.

To day a holly bush entwined with mistletoe grows over the graves of Úna and Tomás. On Christmas Eve the bush is covered in myriads of red berries that open and weep a red sap. The stone over the grave is now intermingled within the holly bush. The tree of life grew from the berries that Tomás brought that Christmas Eve to his Úna.

Should you find their graves then thread softly, softly. Do not cry for Úna and Tomás, for they have found happiness in their devoted love for each other.

'Tread softly o'er our charnel home,
As through this island you're want to roam.
Neither touch the holly nor mistletoe,
That entwined in ivy serendipity grow.'

The lonely grave
Louie Byrne ©

THE MONKS DILEMMA

The bell it tolled in the old churchyard,
In hooded cowl the monk prayed hard.
A crust of bread, a jug of mead;
Oh! Lord have mercy please send me?

That night he prayed on bended knees,
His rosary hung like crying tears.
As in despair and hunger deep,
He cried his tears in humble grief.

He raised his eyes his God to meet,
Rising he sat on the old stone seat:
Oh God! Forgive me all my sins,
For I am poor, my frame is thin.

Ghostly shadows crossed his path,
He knew relief had come at last.
His crucifix he lifted high,
He blessed each one and gave a sigh.

Unable now to kneel and pray,
He tried to leave, no longer stay.
He closed his eyes unable to rise:
Relief it came as the old monk died.

LOUIE BYRNE©

The Passing

As I passed the church I heard the bell,
It tolled three times; then stopped to tell,
My friend had died, that's what it said:
As the Priest with bible the last rites read.

So many times in recent years,
I've heard that bell, know what it means.
Another friend, there's no relief,
A passing soul, heart-rending grief.

I count each day; a saving grace,
The hourglass empties, I cannot stay.
The reaper's come, he's grim and bland,
The glass now empty, there is no sand.

'Tis then the solemn bell I hear,
If saved from guilt I need not fear.
Nor does the thought distressing be,
For I know to day it tolls for me.

LOUIE BYRNE©

39

THE ACE OF SPADES

You count your wealth, unlike the dead,
They know the score; the book is read.
The reaper grim stands outside your door,
The hourglass empties, he calls you home.

You lie abed, and take your ease!
You spread your limbs and are at peace.
The poor souls do so, never more!
Their spirits move from door to door.

Five boards, and one white sheet they have,
A wisp of straw beneath their head's
Five foot of earth to fill their grave
These are the riches of the dead!'

Did I not warn you about carrying a deck of cards in ones pocket? If you took little or no notice of my warning then read on...
It happened in Limerick City on a night in the month of November in the year 1890 on the banks of the Abbey River...

Pat Slattery, a well seasoned gambler and debaucher had lost most of his money in a late nights gambling. Cursing his bad luck he swore that he would be back to have his revenge. His belly was warm with his share of the barrel of ale that he and his companions had consumed that night. He placed his well-worn deck of cards into the pocket of his coatamore. Leaving Johns Square via the Citadel he staggered down Cornwallis Street and wended his way into the 'Irish Town'. At Charlotte's Quay he sat down on a bollard and surveyed the Abbey River as it wended its way to join the majestic Shannon River.
"I would sell my soul if only I could read the cards before they were dealt." He mused as he fumbled with the cards in his pocket.
On the quay wall sat a huge rat preening himself. Pat watched him in the waning moonlight, before the rat took himself off into the river.
He was about to rise from the bollard when he saw a tall gentleman walking along George's Quay on the other side of the riverbank. On his head he wore a tall silk hat that sparkled in the moonlight as he

40

moved. *Around his neck was a white silk cravat. His cloak was a black as a raven's wing and as he walked it opened to reveal a red silk lining that flashed radiant in the moonlight. He watched for some time as the gentleman walked nonchalantly along the opposite quay. A gentleman of wealth on his way home to his wife, no doubt from a transitory night with a lady of ill repute, thought Pat.*

As he moved out of his vision Pat could still hear his feet beat out a steady tattoo on the cobbled street. Looking towards St Mary's Cathedral he once again saw the stranger pass Quay gate and on towards Matthew bridge. The rhythm of his step was as predictable as that of a soldier as he came down the quay to where Pat was seated.

"Now what would a gentleman be doing out in the city at such an hour?" He thought.

"Good evening, Pat Slattery." The gentleman lifted his hat in salutation as he stopped beside Pat.

"Good evening to your good self Sir!" Pat rose from his seat out of respect.

"How do you know my name, have we met before?" Pat queried.

"I have a little time to pass before the dawn breaks, would you like to try
your dexterity at the cards?" The stranger ignoring Pat's question produced a deck of cards from beneath his cloak.

"I'd like to oblige you, but I lost all playing this evening. Perhaps another time." Pat apologised.

"Don't worry my friend, here I will loan you two sovereigns." He shuffled the cards at such speed that Pat hardly noticed.

Taking the two sovereigns from the hand of the stranger, he was surprised that they were very hot, very hot indeed.

Pat rubbed some life into his chilled hands with the coins and picked up the hand that the gentleman dealt him.

He smiled as he deliberated over it. He could hardly believe his eyes. His luck had changed for the better. In his palm he held a full house.

"What have you got?" Pat placed the two sovereigns on the bollard and studied his opponent.

"You beat me fair and square, beginners luck, no doubt." Laughed the gentleman as he exposed his hand.

The first hand and the second went to Pat as did the sixth and seventh.

"You are on to a winning streak Pat. You look chilled, let us pause and have a drink." The gentleman invited.

From beneath his cloak he procured a silver flask and handed it to Pat. Putting the flask to his lips Pat gratefully partook of the contents.

"That is the most sophisticated and sweetest whiskey that ever crossed a man's palate." Pat was one for the fancy words.

"Drink some more Pat, there is an abundance." No matter how much he drank from the flask it never seemed to empty.

"Keep the flask, it is yours. A gift from me to you." The gentleman beamed a beguiling nonchalant smile.

"Thank you very much Sir that is indeed very civil of you. Fancy another game?" Pat was sure that his luck was holding. Once again the cards were dealt and hearts were called. The gentleman laid a Jack but Pat outshone him with his king. Pat led with his queen and drew the gentleman's nine. Once again he was on to a winning streak. Thirteen hands he won in a straight row. Such good fortune he had never known before. His pockets were jingling with silver coins.

"It is time that we finished the game Pat." The gentleman picked up the deck of cards and baited Pat as he shuffled them under his nose.

"They were a fortuitous deck of cards for me, would you consider selling them?" Pat asked.

"Of course, what price would you be willing to pay?" The gentleman asked.

"A sovereign would be a fair price, I'm thinking?" Was Pat's opening offer.

"Not so Pat, these cards could make you a very rich man, a very rich man indeed as they have this night." Pat licked his lips as he saw the gentleman once again temptingly shuffle the cards.

"For a deck of cards such as those I'd sell my soul, so I would." Pat spoke without thought or meaning.

"Would you indeed Pat Slattery, would you indeed?" The gentleman held the pack out to him."

"I would, so I would, believe you me." Pat held out his sweating and shaking hand towards the deck of cards. "Then they are yours Pat Slattery, a deal is a deal is it not?" The gentleman smiled and handed the deck to him. One of the cards fell from the pack as they were being handed over and landed on the quay. The card was the ace of spades.

42

Reaching down to pick it up he noticed that the feet of the man were now those of the beast.

Blessing himself he rose to his full height and looked directly into the eyes of the stranger. A transformation had taken place for now they were as red as brimstone.

"Pick up the card Pat Slattery. Pick it up now." The gentleman's mood changed. He held out his hand and ordered Pat to do his bidding. Pat would have none of it for he knew that if he did then the deal would be executed. The devil would gain his soul. He stood in dread as he was being intimidated before the demon from hell. He was nauseated by the smell of sulphur coming off his cloak. A cold sweat formed on his brow. He tried to pray but the words died on his lips. Then he heard a distant cock heralding in the dawn.

The stranger covered himself with his cloak and letting out a scream vanished into the night. The cards were nowhere to be seen.

He raced across Rutland Street and on into Patrick Street. Down Francis Street he ran never stopping until he reached Arthur Quay.

The Shannon River was lapping the quayside. Pat took his own well-worn deck of cards from his pocket and threw them into the tide followed by the flask. Reaching once again into his pocket he withdrew the coins and threw them into the river after the flask. As they came to rest on the water they turned into dead leaves and floated away on the ebb tide.

Pat returned to the bosom of his family a chastised man. He became a member of the brothers of the Franciscans and a devoted husband. Never did he touch a drop of the amber nectar nor gamble again. Should you wander down Charlotte Quay in Limerick ask the locals to show you the place where the old Tivoli cinema once stood. Near to the quay wall you can still see the burnt marks on the ground where the DEVIL played cards with Pat Slattery that night so long ago.

Shure I'd take you there myself and down the many other walks I mention in my stories only I'm so far away. I know them all for was I not born and bred in the ould city?

THE MORAL OF THIS STORY IS THAT YOU SHOULD NEVER CARRY A DECK OF CARDS IN YOUR POCKET. YOU MAY MEET OLD NICK HIMSELF WHO WILL GAMBLE WITH YOU FOR YOUR SOUL.........YOU HAVE BEEN WARNED.

THE LITTLE URCHIN

The youth in confession took his place,
With penitence written upon his face.
"Bless me father, for I have sinned;"
That little urchin at the Priest did grin.

With down cast eyes he humbly prayed,
His innocent soul he hoped to save.
As one by one his sins he told;
And felt relief, his grief unfold.

He paused, then with a final sigh,
"That's all my sins." He humbly cried.
Absolve me father, please set me free."
The old clock chimed the hour of three.

In nostalgic dreams the old Priest smiled,
As before him knelt an innocent child.
He remembered a time, so long ago;
When he too knelt, his sins unfold.

"How many times?" The cleric asked;
"Twelve times or more." He faced the task,
The wise old cleric scratched his head,
"We'll double the score;" that's what he said.

LOUIE BYRNE©

44

THE SILVER SHILLING.

'Beside a gorse bush sat a Girrfaid small,
With head drooped down he mournfully called.
The sleadóir he crossed himself,
Did this foretell impending death?'

In my time I have meandered through three parts of the county Donegal. It is a wild and beautiful place, filled with the abandoned cottages of a noble people forced to flee their land through hunger and want. The skeletons of the cottages long forsaken have within them the ghosts of the former occupants and the Sean Scéals. The eerie lament of the albatross who is condemned to wander the earth forever more, is all that can be heard in parts. It was around a turf fire in a humble cottage in the northern most reaches of the county in a place named Culdaff that the following Sean Scéal was related by a Sean boct Scéaluide (Poor Old Storyteller)...

In the north of the country in the county Donegal there lived a fine old couple. Their names were Mary and Patrick Slattery. Their children had long since emigrated to America leaving them alone on their poor land outside the village. Beside the cottage ran a neat little river after which the village was named...

It was indeed a wild place and remote, and as such had a beauty that one can only find in such hungry savage lands. But beautiful scenery never put a meal into a hungry belly nor boiled the pot. It was on a day that Pat was out cutting a section of the bog that it happened...

The bog is a lonely and mysterious place. As 'Jack-O-Lantern crosses the bog, it is the wise one that will cross themselves. Ignore the flittering shadows and moans of the bog at your peril. Listen to what I tell you and don't be so smart. May God put some sense into your foolish head of yours and guide your meandering thoughts.

Pat was deep inside the cutting throwing the sods on to the bank when he heard it. It was crooning and a singing mixed, a kind of a dirge. What he heard he had hoped never to hear. Pat thinking that it was the cry of the wandering ghostly albatross, which predicted a death, made the sign of the cross on his forehead before he stuck his head over the bank and looked around him. All he could see was a girrfiad sitting beside a gorse bush preening himself, or so it appeared. Taking little notice of the hare and thinking that it was all in his mind he returned to his task. He knew that bogs were strange places indeed

45

and that Jack-O-Lantern had the habit of playing tricks on any lone *sleadóir (Turf cutter)*. Before he had time to put his foot on the *slán (Spade)* he again heard the dirge.

"Jesus, Mary and holy Saint Joseph protect me." Making the sign of the cross he prayed.

Curiosity getting the better of him he came out of the bog and again looked all 'round him. The only sign of life was the hare standing upright in the same spot. He decided that he would go and investigate. Why the hare did not run away when he saw him he could not understand? As both he and Mary were partial to a drop of stew he took his *slán* intending to kill it for the pot. Making the sign of the cross on his forehead he slowly crept across to where the hare was standing upright, motionless. He was surprised that he still made no effort to escape. Raising his *slán* he was about to bring it down on its head when lo and behold the hare looked up at him with sorrowful tears in his eyes.

"Kill me! You may as well, there is nothing for me to live for." He pleaded.

"God bless us and save us, is that yourself talking?" Dropping the spade he blessed himself and stood mortified looking down at the hare.

"There's no mistake I can assure you. It's myself that's doing the talking, Pat Slattery. Take your spade and put an end to me." The hare pleaded as he shook the dew from off his back.

"Shure I'm not that heartless, although my stomach is touching my backbone with the hunger. I could no more kill you without as much as a how-do-you do, no more than I could my good woman." Pat leaning on his *slán* looked down at the poor miserable hare.

"If I turn my back will you kill me then?" Again the hare pleaded.

"No! I will not, whatever do you think I am? Come now! Tell me what this is all about, I'm all ears?" Pat laid his spade to one side and sat on a flat *carriag (rock)*

"It all happened last night I tell you as I was going to the *srúil (stream)* below Gleneely. You know the place, of that I have no doubt?"

"Sure! Sure I know it, but get on with the story." Pat was impatient to hear the story.

46

"Well! It's like this as I was taking a drink, did not a cruel buitre (witch) come up behind me and for no reason at all, no reason at all I tell you, turn me into a hare."

"If you are not a hare, what are you then?" Pat queried.

"I'm a clúracan, did I not tell you?"

"Well, you are the first one of them fellows that I ever met. Bless my old caubeen, a leprechaun by all the saints. A leprechaun, me Pat Slattery talking to a leprechaun. Tell me was it the ould hag from Limerick that done it?" Pat looked cautiously across the bog.

"Will you stop your shenanigans and never mind the niceties. How would I know who she was or where she came from? Can you be of assistance to me? My life is not worth a tinkers curse out here in the open as you saw for yourself?" He pleaded.

"Well now, what would it be worth to me if I could help you?" Pat smiled down at the little fellow.

"I'll give you a shilling piece, so I will." Promised the leprechaun.

"A shilling is it now. Is this all your life is worth?" Pat placed his hands on his hips and studied the (hare) leprechaun.

"This is no ordinary shilling, for you can never spend it."

"Never mind the compensation for now. How may I assist you?"

"As you see I cannot move from where I sit. The buitre left me here in this position. Fair game to any sleador, hawk or madra rúah (Fox) for that matter come to think of it. So, you see I am at your mercy."

"Never let it be said that Pat Slattery denied a favour to a fellow traveller. So long as the Ould hag from Limerick is not involved, I'll help. She's a bad bitch is that one. I might even gain an indulgence, if you get my meaning?" Pat stood up and stuck out his chest.

"I guarantee you Pat, she had nothing to do with my situation. Now will you take me to the pool below the lady rock in the great lake and dip me three times in it? Then if you give me a real good shake I should be back to me old self and as right as rain."

"If a good soaking and shake will give you some comfort then I'm your man." Pat picked up the hare by the scruff of his neck. Taking him to the lake he gave him three good duckings in the pool and afterwards a right good shaking. Having finished the task he laid the exhausted hare on the ground. When Pat looked down the second time he saw a clúracan lying there and he as naked as the day that he was born.

"Pat Slattery! That was one good shaking and I am beholding to you. Would you excuse me now while I fetch my bríste fada (Long trousers) and caipéan dearg?" (Red Cap) Away went the fairy and Pat looked after him cursing himself for being so credulous.

"Sure it was my only chance in life to get a crock of gold and I was too trusting." He muttered to himself.

"Did you say something, Pat Slattery?" Looking behind him he saw the fairy adjusting his breeches.

"To be nothing but honest; I thought that I had seen the last of you."

"I'm a man of my word, so I am. Here is the shilling that I promised you. Guard it well and spend it wisely for one day the debt will be paid in full." With that he handed Pat the promised shilling.

"Fare thee well Pat Slattery, your pot will be forever overflowing and your belly full. Our paths will cross again when you least expect them." With these predictions the fairy was off. Pat returned home and told Mary of his adventures.

"You've not been over to Louie's for a drop of the hard stuff Pat, (Poteén) tell me?" She pleaded on hearing the story.

"Mary allanah! Here is the shilling that he gave me. Now where would I get a shilling and me with not enough money to buy a scrap of tobac (tobacco) to fill me old cré dúidín (pipe)?"

"You'll have your tobac Pat so you will and a glass to quench your thirst." Putting her shawl round her shoulders and then over her head she invited him to join her. Together they went into the village. They sat one each side of the fire in the pub owned by Louie Byrne. Each supped a glass of porter as they chatted like two doves on the same branch. Pat had his broken clay piópa stuck in the side of his gob and Mary was taking the pinch of snuff from her tin box.

"Pat, I hate to see you with an empty glass in your hand but the shilling is long spent. Louie is not one to give credit on the slate. We should be making tracks back home so we should." Rising from their stools they bid good night to their host and returned home.

"I enjoyed to night, so I did Pat, and all thanks to your friend the leprechaun." Mary remarked as they wended their way up the old boréen to their cottage. It did not take a lot to please the old couple.

Next morning Pat put on his breeches and came out of the bedroom and sat eating his gruel.

"Do you know Mary, it was little reward I got for the services I gave to that Clúracan?" He was regretting his folly for not insisting on a better deal.

"Pat Slattery, thank God for yesterday. Don't you know the powers them little fellows have? Why! You could be walking around this blessed day with a hump on your back, so you could. Be thankful for small mercies. By the way don't let anyone hear you tell of talking to a leprechaun, they'd think you were losing the mind." She warned.

"You're right Mary, 'tis sorry I am for being so selfish, forgive me love, we should indeed count our blessings." Pat rose from the table and went across to the mantle. Taking his cré duidin from the shelf he reached into his pocket hoping to find a scrape of tobacco.

"Mary will you ever look at this?" He removed his hand from his pocket and held out his open palm for her to see.

"What is it Pat, nothing wrong I hope?" Showing her concern she came across the kitchen and looked at his palm.

"It's a shilling and it sitting in my pocket, where could it have come from? Did we not spend the only shilling we had yesterday?"

"Did you not tell me that the fairy told you the shilling could never be spent?" She reminded him.

"So he did Mary, so he did. We must keep this to ourselves, so we must. If the parish Priest heard of this, God only knows what he'd say. Now there is gratitude for you, and me upset for not getting more from the little fellow. I must apologies if ever I see him again." He remarked full of remorse.

Time went by and with their new found wealth they built a fine new cottage with a stone floor and a warm hearth. They were able to pay the fare for their children to return to their home in Ireland. There was full contentment in the home of the Slattery family, I can assure the reader. They thanked their God that there would never be the 'American wake' in the Slattery household again. Not mind you that they ever forgot those in need. They were most charitable to the stranger who came knocking at their door.

Pat and Mary finally went away in the city of Dublin for a well-deserved holiday. They had never seen the fine city and this was their chance. Their son David was looking after the cottage in their absence. It was a cantankerous day and David could do nothing but dream away the time in front of a roaring turf fire. He listened to the wind in the chimney and was about to doze off when...'

Hearing a knocking on the half door he rose from his leaba suidheacan (Settled bed) and opened the half door.

"Tar isteac agus a céad míle fáilte roath" (Come in and a thousand welcomes) he greeted the caller.

"Mait an lá leat a duine usail. (Good day to you kind person) Could you spare a copper for a poor 'Fear an botar' (man of the road)?" A little man stuck his head over the half door, shaking with the cold.

"To be shure, tar isteac, tar isteac (Come in, come in) and take the weight off your feet." David invited.

The little man reached up and opening the bolt of the lower half of the door entered the kitchen.

"It's a fine house you have here, so it is. And with as fine a stone floor as ever I saw for the dancing." The little man remarked as he danced a few steps, trying out the floor as one might say.

"Pull a stooléen up to the fire, I'll fetch you something to eat." David offered. Being a charitable man, like his parents he set a meal out for the little man.

"You're more than kind, so you are." The little man remarked on finishing the meal. He rose from the chair with some effort on account of being so small and his belly being so full.

"Here put this in your pocket and welcome." David picked up the shilling that was lying on the shelf above the fireplace and gave it to the little fellow.

"That is indeed more than generous of you, are you sure you want to part with it?" The little fellow bemused asked.

"It's not that much, Father always keeps it on the mantle. Why I'll never know. Perhaps he is keeping it for a rainy day. Take it and may good luck follow you and it." David spat on the coin for good luck before he handed it over.

"Thanking you again kind sir! You'll never know how true your words are. Never will the pot be empty in the Slattery household, of that be assured. Would you ever tell your father that the hare from the lady pool is fit and well?" He foretold.

"Do you know my father then, what might be your name for the asking?"

"Just give him the message and I'll be beholding to you."

50

Pat and Mary returned from the great city and spent the afternoon telling their sons of the wonderful sights that met their eyes.

"It was a holiday that I'll never forget, thanks Pat." Mary smiled as she pushed the crane holding the kettle over the fire.

"Don't be thanking me, allanah (Love). Thank the leprechaun and his shilling." Taking a piece of turf in the tongs he lit his piopca. Pat reached up and began to search the mantle piece for his shilling. Unable to find it he stood up on the stool and looked all along the shelf. The shilling had gone.

"Mary, did you take our shilling?" In great agitation he continued to search along the mantle without success.

"The fairy shilling is it. I'd never touch it?"

"Someone has taken it for sure." Pat looked worried.

"Ask David, he must have moved it and put it some place safe?" She assured him.

"Son, did you see an old shilling piece that was sitting on the mantle?" His father asked him on his return from the village.

"That old shilling on the mantle? Why I gave it to a little man of the roads. He called in for a meal and the 'craic'. He was reluctant to take it. When I pressed it on him he smiled and thanking me informed me that he owed his life to you."

"Sure I never saved anyone's life, what was his name?"

"He never did tell me his name but he told me to tell you that the hare from the lady pool was fit and well."

Pat looked at Mary and they both began to laugh. They now had enough in life without the need for the shilling.

"He'll have another poor créatur in mind for it, so he will." Pat went to the half door and lifting his cap in salutation looked deep into the distant mountains.

You may think that you don't believe in fairies... Yet would you destroy a fairy Hawthorne tree or not carry a charm of sorts? ...

Thank God I'm an atheist? Think!

FAR AWAY ON THE FOOT OF THE BLUE STACK MOUNTAINS SAT A CLÚRACAN TOSSING A SHILLING INTO THE AIR AND LAUGHING TO HIMSELF.

THE POOR CLARE NUN

Remember Mary, the day that we met?
The sun played host where we two sat:
You looked so radiant, gave me a smile,
That will live with me 'till the day I die.
I knew you not, yet my heart stood still;
That pleasant evening by the old flour Mill.

When you left my love, you took my soul;
And left me stranded on a barren shore:
On our seat I sat in sunshine and shower,
I waited my love, beneath that old bower.
I heard the waters, the mill stream fill;
Not far from our seat by the old flour Mill.

'I saw you Mary, 'twas some way off,
And knew my love you had not forgot.'
I held your gentle hands in mine;
And kissed your lips as a goblet of wine.
I heard the Lark and Linnet sing,
As I courted you beside the old flour Mill.

You told me that evening, I remember it well;
Of a love that was greater, a calling you said.
In betrayal and anger, I pushed you away;
What reason I felt, was for me to stay?
My love and devotion was all there to give,
You scorned that love beside the old flour Mill.

I turned my back, how could I stay?
I saw in your eyes the message that said,
'I now love another, forgive me my friend;
I'll think of you often alone in my cell?'
The hate in my heart my eyes it did fill,
The night you betrayed me beside the old flour Mill.

52

I fretted, I worried, I knew you'd not stay;
You'd leave me in sorrow. You'd send me away.
I cursed your sweet vows, your devoted faith;
You left me, my darling in ungracious haste:
To the nuns of the Poor Clare your love to give,
And leave me in sorrow beside the old flour Mill.

I saw you that day, you were dressed in white;
A bride I was told, a bride for our Christ:
The door it was closed and a grid did appear,
Did you think of me Mary? Did you know I was near?
"I'll not forget you Mary, nor the love that we filled,
And the vows that we pledged by the old flour Mill.

I still see you Mary, through my tears and my pain;
Why! Why did you leave me another to gain?
I hear your voice, mo chúsla, in the silent night;
I walk in your shadow by moonlight bright:
My joy knew no bounds, the earth it stood still;
As we kissed and we cuddled beside the old flour Mill.

For you my beloved I've given my life,
You told me my darling for you I was right.
We sealed our devotion, we never would part;
Our bodies entwined in one beating heart.
My mind is tormented the last hour that I fill,
Remember me Mary beside the old flour Mill.
They say time is a healer. Past to be forgot;
Yet my hearts' not relinquished that bonded knot.
My sleep is disturbed, my life's in tatters.
Who cares? Who worries, what does it matter?
The water runs deep, for life I've no will,
Pray for me Mary beside the old flour Mill.

Louie **Byrne**

53

The Tinker

Tinker coming down the street;
To your homes beat a retreat.
Don't you dare your mother tell;
Never mind the goods she sells.

Run! Run lets make haste,
She's gaining ground, are we too late?
A shade of sourness upon her face,
Just look at her, she's not our race?

Close the door and stay inside,
Peep through curtains as you hide.
Look! She's standing at the gate?
Her basket filled, just let her wait.

Plastic flowers, wooden pegs for sale,
She holds them up, her feet are bare.
The shawl she wears is Galway grey;
A baby gurgles and has no cares.

She pauses at the open gate;
Close the curtain hide your face.
Soon she'll tire, be on her way,
Then open the door and resume our play.

LOUIE BYRNE©

THE CHILDREN OF LIR

No seanachai worth his/her salt would omit this old Irish legend from their books. Here then is my translation of this ancient Celtic legend. I hope you will enjoy it...

Long, long age in the mystic age beyond a thousand, thousand years, Ireland was ruled by a magical race of people. They were the Tutan de Dannan. To day we know them as fairies. They were the warriors of Éireann long before the Celts secured their final resting place at Clonmacnoise.
To day they sleep beneath the Cromlechs, Dolmens, Mehirs and Tumuli. These, one can find scattered throughout the length and breadth of Ireland. Their large flat stone standing on three stone legs identify most. They are not graves, as we know them, but the resting places of the Tuatan de Dannan. The story unfolds...

King Lir was a Dannan and as such he could not die for they were Gods who reigned on earth for a long period of time before hibernating into the long sleep.
The Tuatan de Dannan decided that instead of having five kings ruling independently over their own kingdoms, they would have one Árd Rí (High king). The others would be subjugate to his wise council. The kings went into conference and debated as to who was the wisest to become their Árd Rí. After long deliberations they selected Bodh Dearg (Bodh the red). All were delighted with the arrangement with the exception of King Lir. He was the noblest of the kings and a Sidhe Fionna (White fairy). He refused to pay homage to the new Árd Rí and returned to his kingdom at Lake Derryvaragh in the county now known as Westmeath. His ill manners caused great upset and the council wanted to burn Lir's palace and put him to death. That was impossible for Lir was of the Tuatan de Dannan and a powerful king and could not be destroyed except by the Gods.
Bodbh Dearg knew of this and restrained his subjects, telling them that there would be great sorrow on their part were they to attempt this. They greeted this wise decision with acclaim.

King Bodbh Dearg returned to Limerick and set up his court at a great lake at Killaloe and called it after himself. Lough Dearg.

A misfortune was however to befall King Lir. His young wife was called away by the Gods to the long sleep. Lir was devastated for he loved his wife dearly.

King Bodbh heard of the grief of Lir and decided to offer him the hand of friendship.

"I am the foster father of the beautiful daughters of king Aillil of the islands of Achill, they are staying with me at present. Send a messenger to king Lir and tell him that I wish to speak to him on a matter of great importance."

Lir on receiving the message and fearing a trap set out with a great army. Arriving on the shore of Lough Dearg he made camp. King Bodbh came in person to the lakeside and addressed Lir.

"I come in peace King Lir of Lake Derryvaragh. If you submit to the decision of the council and accept me as the Árd Rí, I will give to you one of the daughters of King Aillil as you queen."

Lir accepted and paid due allegiance to the Árd Rí.

Bodbh laid on a great banquet for Lir at his palace. At the high table sat King Bodbh and his queen. To the left and right of them sat the daughters of King Aillil. There was Niamh, Aoife and Arbha. These were the most beautiful virgins in the entire kingdom.

Lir looked in wonderment at the beautiful girls. Never had he seen such radiant beauty.

"Pick who you will Lir. For whoever you choose then she will be your wife." Bodbh promised him.

Lir looked from one to the other but could not make his mind up. They all were worthy of a great king, such as he.

After some deliberation he decided that he would take the eldest Niamh to be his bride.

The wedding was held at the great palace at Killaloe. Lir and his wife remained there for a year and a day before returning to Lake Derryvaragh.

It was over this enchanted land that King Lir and his queen Niamh ruled. They had two beautiful children. Fionnuala their princess and Aedh their prince. The people prospered under the wise leadership of Lir and the country was at peace.

56

One afternoon their mother called her children to her side and told them that she was again with child. The children were delighted for her and their father.

Scouts were sent far and wide throughout the kingdom to proclaim the good news. Several months later the queen went into labour and gave birth to twins. Both were boys.

"Your mother has given birth to twin boys and we have named them Fiacra and Conn." Their father informed them. The children were excited and wanted to go at once to congratulate their mother and see the twins.

"I have to attend to matters of state and regrettably I cannot take you to see the twins." The king informed them.

"Oh father please! Let us have just a little peep at them." Pleaded Fionnuala.

"Very well then, but remember you must be ever so quiet. Mechair will take you to your mother." Mechair was the faithful servant of the king.

The children hopped and skipped along the long passages to the room where their mother and the twins were resting. At the door to the room, Mechair put his finger to his lips and called on the children to be quiet. They were to wait outside until they were called into the bedchamber.

Mechair knocked gently on the door and waited. Then turning the handle he opened the door gently and called to his queen. There was no reply; all was quiet in the room.

"My queen, it is I, Mechair. Your children are anxious to visit you and the twins." There was an uncanny silence in the room. Mechair slowly approached the bed. He paused and looked again only this time in shock and sorrow. The queen lay silent on the bed. The Gods had called her to the long sleep.

He retreated from the room and closed the door. Then he called the children to his side.

"Fionnuala go! Go at once and ask your father to come to the bed chamber." There was urgency in his voice.

Leaving the affairs of state, The king rushed from the assembly room. He knew that Mechair would not disturb the royal court when in session unless it was important.

At the bedside Lir held his wife's hand for the last time and looked in sorrow at her beautiful face. Cradled in her right hand was Conn and in her left hand Fiacra.

"Your mother has gone to rest for a time." He told the two children. The Tuathan de Dannan race cannot die, they go to the kingdom of the Gods to rest before they are reborn.

"Fionnuala, You are my eldest. You must grow quickly to womanhood. You will be mother to the twins, Conn and Fiacra."

"You my eldest son, Aedh, will from this time on instruct them in the ways and customs of the Tuatan de Dannan. For you will be king one day when I am no longer of this earth." The king embraced his children.

Then he turned to Mechair, who was standing some distance away.

"Come! Come and give me you allegiance Mechair. You, my long and trusted servant, I place the safety of all my children into your care."

Mechair grasped the hilt of his sword and knelt on the ground before his king.

"My king, your wish is my command. I will faithfully carry out the trust that you have placed in me. This I swear for as long as I have breath in my mortal body. This I swear." Clasping his fist to his breast he accepted the challenge willingly.

The king went across to where his queen lay and kneeling beside the bed began to weep.

The children were shocked at this, for their father was never known to cry.

"We must leave them alone, for soon the Gods will call to carry your mother to the place of the long sleep." Mechair guided the children from the room and gently closed the door leaving the king to his sorrow.

Chapter Two.

The king could not be consoled, nor could he accept that his queen had been called back to the kingdom of the Gods.

"Why did they do this to me? I never offended them." He asked Mechair time and time again.

"It is the wish of the Gods, Sire. We must not question them. Do not challenge the wishes of the Gods." Mechair advised and warned him.

In deep sorrow and anger at the Gods he neglected the affairs of state. The Royal chambers had not had an assembly since queen Niamh went for her long sleep to the kingdom of the Gods. He spent most of his time in her empty room. The Gods had called as he slept and taken her away. He was waiting for the day when the Gods would release her from the great sleep. But the Gods did not return her.

In deep sorrow he took himself off to the great summer palace on Lough Derryvaragh and became a recluse.

His subjects noticed the change in their king and they too began to neglect their duties. The kingdom was slowly disintegrating.

All through this sad period of mourning, Mechair continued to look after the welfare of the children.

Once again King Bodbh sent his messengers to the palace of King Lir. He would not be allowed to suffer the pangs of loneliness any longer. He was invited to come to the palace of Bodbh at once.

Lir ordered that the royal barge be made ready. He was going to visit Bodbh Dearg, his father-in-law. He spent the next three months at Bodbh's palace and could be seen walking in the gardens with his sleeping queens' sister, Aoife. He seemed to be more his old self. Once again he took up his duties and the country returned to normal. He continued to spend most of his time at the palace of Bodbh and in the company of Aoife.

Then one afternoon Bodbh ordered that a great banquet be prepared at the palace, a month and a day from that day.

He sent messengers to all the chieftains throughout the land. They were to assemble he commanded at a great banquet for a very important announcement.

King Lir returned to his own palace and called on Mechair to bring his children to his side.

"As you know children, I have been in mourning for a long period of time for my queen, your mother. I was a very lonely king and this was affecting my nation and moreso your welfare."

"We know and understand father." Fionnuala spoke for all the children.

"I love your mother and always will, but the God's have not returned her. We must let her rest as they command."

Lir told them no more. They were to accompany him to the palace of Bodbh at Lough Dearg.

When Lir approached the palace a great keening was heard in sympathy of his plight. The keening continued for a further three weeks.

By this time the great banquet was about to take place. The chieftains from all the provinces of Ireland were now assembled. They were there to pay homage to the Árd Rí Bodbh and to hear the royal proclamation.

King Bodbh and King Lir sat side by side at the great table on the occasion of the banquet. To the left and right sat the remaining daughters of King Aillil.

After the great banquet and before the merriment came about the Ard Ri rose from his seat. He looked down at his assembled subjects.

"King Lir, ruler of the Sidhe Fionna has suffered a deep depression at the loss of his queen Niamh. His kingdom has suffered as a consequence and so has he and his children. It is in our power and in our hearts to alleviate his sorrow. I have therefore decided to give Aoife to him to be his new queen." There was a great hush in the hall for a moment or two. Then the whole hall echoed to the sounding of trumpets and blaring of horns. The assembly cheered and banged the table with their goblets to show their approval.

Aoife was indeed a beautiful woman and worthy of the highest office.

On the day Lir and Aoife were joined together there was merriment throughout the kingdom. That evening as the sun sank in the west and a harvest moon rose in the sky, beacons were lit from one end of the land to the other. This to proclaim that they now had a new queen.

"Aoife! But father what of our mother?" Aedh asked afterwards.

"Mother is someone special and our love for her will never wane. I told you that she is with the Gods. I ask you, will you give some of your love to Aoife?" The king pleaded with his children. He would never do anything to hurt them.

"Father, we will give of our love to Aoife, but we will keep a special place for mother until she returns." Fionnuala the eldest and wisest spoke.

King Lir and his espouse Aoife were wed at a great banquet given by King Bodhe at his palace at Killaloe.

The queen took a great interest in the children and could be seen in their company on most days. All seemed at peace within the kingdom.

King Lir was now a changed man and ruled his kingdom as only a wise king could.

CHAPTER THREE

A year and a day after the fairy tale union between King Lir and his new queen Aoife, a change was noticed in the queen. She now began to find fault with everything that the children did. They tried to please her by accepting that no matter what went against the queens' wishes was their fault. They promised to do their best to please her. Their appeasement was to no avail.

She went to the king one day and demanded that Mechair be removed from his office of guardian to the children. The king was horrified at such a suggestion and refused. Aoife got into a rage and told the king that he loved his children more than he loved her.

Mechair on hearing the moods and tantrums of the queen was now worried for the welfare of the children. What could he do? She was his queen, yet he had a sworn duty to his king and the children.

As the days went into weeks he got more and more worried. He could not watch the children day and night. He also knew that Aoife could not kill the children, for they were of the Tuatan-de-Dannan race and could not die. He knew that Aoife had powerful magic and he feared that she would use this to do harm to them.

Mechair went to see one of the ancient Druids of learning to seek his advice and to find out if he could appease Aoife in any way. He was shocked to learn that Aoife had consulted with the druids and asked when she may expect to be with child. The druids told her that she would remain barren forever.

On hearing this devastating news Aoef flew into an uncontrollable rage and rushing headlong from the consultation vowed vengeance on the children of Lir.

"What can I do to defend them for the queen is a powerful sorceress?" Mechair wrung his hands and pleaded for advice.

"Take these stones, for they are the stones of truth. Give one to Fionnula and keep one to yourself. Wherever the children are you will be able to find them." The druid gave Mechair two eye stones on leather necklaces.

Returning to the palace he sought out the children and called them to him.

"Fionnuala, take this and wear it always. It contains all the stories of truth and the first magic of our race. Whenever you need me point the

stone and it will guide me to you. I must warn you not to remove it."
He placed the talisman around Fionnuala's neck and kissed her on
the cheek.

This was most unusual for a servant and the children knew at once
that something evil was about to happen.

Queen Aoife fell into a deep depression and confined herself to her
rooms. She refused to see anyone and demanding that all her needs
were to be brought to her. She stayed shut up in her rooms for a year
and a day.

One summer's morning she made a grand appearance in the garden.
The children hesitated on seeing her, not knowing what to expect.
Opening her arms wide the queen smiled at them. Happily at her
recovery they ran to greet her.

"We are pleased to see that you are well again." Fionnuala greeted
her.

"Thank you, children. To day I am going to take you sailing on the
great lake of Lough Derryvaragh." She told them.

Fionnuala took hold of her talisman and it felt very cold. She ran at
once and told Mechair of the plans their stepmother had for them.

Mechair ran to where the children were assembled and stood beside
them in a defiant stance.

"You can go Mechair, I will look to the children this day." The queen
dismissed him.

Mechair hesitated and stood his ground not knowing what he should
do.

"Mechair, did you not hear me? Be gone this instant." The queen
ordered.

Mechair could do nothing; he had to obey the queen. With a heavy
heart he watched as she led the children out to the courtyard.

The great coach was brought forward and harnessed to two swift
steeds. The children noted that the coach was to be driven by Connan.
He was the manservant of the queen. He was deaf and dumb. He took
his orders from the queen and nobody else. This action by the queen
was most suspicious. Mechair was in charge of the children at all
times. On the kings command he should escort them wherever they
went.

The queen and the children boarded the coach and soon they were out
of view of the palace. Passing along the lakeshore she called on

Connan to rest the horses. The children wanted to go swimming in the lake, she claimed.

"You go and swim children, there is plenty of time yet." The queen instructed them.

"Come sit with me, Connan." The queen, speaking in sign language, invited her servant to join her.

"You are my faithful servant, are you not?" She questioned him as they sat side by side.

"You know me well, my Queen. There is nothing in this world that I would not do for you." Her servant replied in sign language.

"That is what I wanted to hear, Connan. Could you somehow destroy the children of Lir?" The queen looked deep into his eyes.

"Destroy the children of Lir? Never! Never. What are you saying, No! No, I am not hearing this." He spelt out the reply in sign language. Rising to his feet and ran to the coach sobbing.

"Then Connan, you no longer love your queen. You will from this day become a lark, never to land on earth again." Raising her wand she turned him into a lark. Connan now in the form of a lark rose into the sky and began to sigh. He looked down at the children of Lir splashing each other in the water and began to cry. The cry of the lark that is heard to this day is the keening of Connan. Rising high into the sky and with a final sigh he disappeared from the lakeside.

The queen sat down on the side of the lake looking out at the deep waters. She would have to put a charm on the children, for she could not kill them.

Unaware of what was taking place on the shore, the children splashed and swam around in the safety of the shallows. The queen sat watching them and encouraged them to be brave and swim out into deeper waters.

"You are the enchanted children of Lir. You are brave and fearless, swim deeper." She told them. The children swan to the centre of the great lake and looked back towards the shore.

Where had the queen got to? Fionnuala thought, for there was no sign of her. Taking little notice of what she said the others continued to splash and swim.

Aedh was the first to notice that the Queen had returned. She was standing by the waters edge with a wand in her hand. His suspicions aroused he called to his sister and the twins to swim for the shore *immediately. Seeing them approaching she raised her wand and as she did so the children found that they could not move.*

"Your father, King Lir, loves you more than he does me. You will never return to the Kingdom of Lir." Her voice boomed over the lake and reached the ears of the terrified children.

Then a great whirlpool appeared in the lake and the children were dragged down into its depths. Down, down the children were dragged. Fionnuala was vomited from the depths followed by Aedh. She looked at her reflection in the water and was shocked to see that she had been turned into a swan. Looking across the lake she could see another white swan coming towards her.

"It is me Aedh, Look at yourself? The queen has turned us into swans." Aedh looked at his reflection in the water and saw that he too was now a graceful swan.

"Where are the twins? They must have drowned." Aedh cried out. Taking a deep breath he dived deep beneath the waters of the lake and began searching for his brothers.

He found the twins in a tangle of weeds endeavouring to free themselves.

Aedh on seeing their predicament swam to their aid and brought them to the surface.

The twins were most upset and frightened when they saw that their brother and sister were turned into swans.

"Don't be frightened, Mechair will find us. He will know how to reverse the evil spell." Aedh assured the twins.

The twin swans swam towards Fionnuala. Opening her great wings she brought them inside and comforted them.

As the swans sought solace in each other's company their stepmother appeared on the shoreline. From where she addressed the children.

"You will remain as swans for a period of nine hundred years or until you hear the church bells ring. You will spend the first three hundred years of that period on the surface of Lough Derryvaragh. Then you will fly to the Straits of Moyle. There you will spend the next three hundred years. You will spend the following three hundred years in the waters of Erris and Inis Gloria on the western seashore. Then as many years as it takes until the union of Lairgnean the prince of Connaught with Deichthe the princess of Munster.

You will remain as swans until you hear the church bells ring."

The children of Lir listened in shocked silence as Aoife proclaimed her cruel punishment on them.

They did not know what she meant by Church bells, for Christianity was unknown in those days.

They did not understand why this crass punishment was imposed on them. They had done all they could and more to appease their stepmother. Would they ever see their father again? Would they rest in the land of Tir-na-nOg beside other members of the race of Tuatan-de- Dannan? They could only wait and hope.

Although frightened themselves, Fionnuala and Aedh tried not to show it. They did not wish to upset the twins any more than they were at present.

"Why is she punishing us like this?" Conn looked up at Fionnuala and wiped a tear from his eye with his wing.

"Our stepmother thinks that our father loves us more than her. This is her revenge. Don't fret little brother, I'll send for Mechair by pointing the talisman. He will bring father and we will be children again." Conn cheered up on hearing this assurance.

Fiacra, who was swimming near to the shore heard a voice calling their names and began to swim towards the shore.

"No Fiacra! Swim for the reeds and hide it may be a trick." Aedh warned his brother. The swans gathered in the safety of the reed bed and remained very still.

Fionnuala stuck her beak out from the shelter of the reed bed and saw a man on the shore pointing a stone along the bank.

"It's Mechair! We are saved." She whispered to the others.

"We had best be cautious, it may be a trick of the queen. I'll swim towards the man and have a look." Aedh warned.

Mechair saw the swan swimming towards him and presumed that he was looking for food. Ignoring the swan he continued searching along the bank for the children. The big swan kept following him, keeping to the safety of the water. Mechair stopped and looking at the swan, he encouraged him to come to the shoreline.

"Did you see the children of Lir in your travels?" He questioned the swan.

The swan left the water and came to his side and looked deep into his eyes.

"Don't you know what happened here Mechair? I am Aedh, Fionnuala and the twins are hiding in the reed bed. Our stepmother has turned us into swans and inflicted a terrible punishment on us."

"Come to me, it is I, Mechair. Have no fear." Mechair's voice echoed across the lake as he called on the others to join him.

He looked at their sad faces as they came to the waters edge one by one and gathered around him.

"I will go at once to the palace of Bodbh and tell him of this foul deed. The King will know how to reverse the spell, have no fear." He hugged the swans to him and assured them.

"Hurry Mechair! Hurry for the spell is very powerful and is growing more so by the minute." Aedh flapped his wings in agitation.

Mechair wasting no time took the shortest route to the palace.

Entering the palace he was confronted by the servants crying and keening. He was told that the queen had arrived some time previous in great distress and with her clothing in disarray. The children of Lir were no more; wild beasts of the forest she told the assembly had eaten them.

Mechair rushed to the great chamber and was in time to hear Aoife relating her account of what became of the children of Lir.

The children she claimed had gone into the lake to cool off after the long journey. After their swim the children took to playing on the shore. It was then that a pack of wild boar came out of the woods and attacked them. Her servant without fear for his own life attacked the boars with his spear but the fierce animals soon ate him. Then they attacked the children and ate every one of them. She had fought them off bravely and only escaped by hiding in the carriage.

This was indeed a plausible story for there were no witnesses and her face was scratched and her clothes were torn. Anyhow who would believe that the queen would do anything to harm the children of Lir?

"Where were you Mechair when the children of Lir were being attacked?" The king questioned his faithful servant.

"The children of Lir have not been eaten, Sire. Your queen could not kill any of the race of the Tuatan-de -Dannan, so she put a spell on them." Mechair pointed the finger of accusation at the queen.

"What is this insolence, you dare accuse my foster child, the queen?" Bodbh strode towards Mechair. His anger showing.

"Wait! Tell me Aoife why you did not use your magical powers to kill the boars or to turn them into harmless creatures?" King Lir asked.

Queen Aoife ignored the question and repeated her story over and over again.

"Let those of you who doubt my word ride to Lough Derryvaragh. There you will find the children of Lir swimming in the lake. They are now four white swans and are awaiting anxiously for their father to come and remove the evil spell." Mechair interrupted.

"Enough! Enough of this." Bodbh strode from the room only to return carrying the rod of truth.

"Take the rod Aoife and repeat your story. Remember you cannot lie when holding the rod of truth." Bodbh warned.

Aoife took the rod and began her account of the tragedy at Lough Derryvaragh. As she spoke the rod turned into a serpent and told the truth of what happened on the shore of lake Derrvaragh.

Her father was now very angry at what his foster child had done. She was no longer considered a member of the Tuatan-de-Dannan. Taking his wand he approached her and waved it over her. Slowly she seemed to vanish in a maze of colours only to reappear as a large flying insect. Out the window she flew and began to fly towards the lake.

"Stop her! She is flying to the lake." Mechair called.

Bodbh once again waved his wand and a huge eagle came out of the sky and with one swoop picked her up in his talons and took her off. She would make a tasty meal for her young.

Chapter Four

Queen Aoife was now no more, and with her gone it was impossible to unravel the secret spell she had used on the Children of Lir. King Lir called upon the wisest and most powerful of the Druids to come forward and try to unravel the secret of the curse. Try as they may, their efforts were to no avail. He was devastated as he watched his beautiful children swimming to and fro across the lake. He was the most powerful man in the whole kingdom, yet he could do nothing for his children. He blamed himself for the catastrophe that had befallen them.

However deep his grief he would have to do something to add a little comfort to his children's plight.

"Is there nothing that can be done for the children of Lir?" The grief stricken king pleaded

"Nothing I fear, until Lairgnean, the prince from the north of the country joins with Deicthe the princess from the south." He was told.

A great keening was heard wailing over the palace when this was announced. For the children of Lir were favourites of all.

"We will take the children back with us." Lir declared.

"My liege! That too is impossible. The spell is too deep even for you to override it. They must remain on Lough Derryvaragh for three hundred years. The water is now their home and they must not and cannot take up their abode with humans." The druid again informed the king.

As it was impossible to bring the children back to human form nor could they leave the lake, Lir decided that a new palace should and would be built on the lakeshore. There the Royal household would live for the next three hundred years. The finest teachers in the kingdom would educate them. He brought the finest musicians and singers from the four corners of the land to entertain them and to teach them to sing.

It was soon discovered that the children had a talent for singing. People came from far and wide to listen to their melodious voices. All was well in the kingdom of Lir. However time was passing and when one is waiting for time to stand still it passes all the quicker.

The children noticed that their old tutors and friends were becoming less and less. Many had gone to the place of the long sleep. They would not return to Tír- na- nÓg for many hundred of years.

One evening as the sun was setting in the evening sky and the children were returning to their haven, they heard a voice calling to them.

"Children of Lir! Can you bide awhile?" A old man crippled with age hobbled to the shoreline and leaning on his stick awaited their arrival.

"It is you Mechair, what troubles you?" Aedh asked.

"Children, I have been your guardian for more than three hundred years. My body is racked with pain and I can hardly see. I am no longer capable of guarding you. I should have gone to the place of the long sleep many years ago. I was waiting and hoping that the spell might be broken and that you would return. Alas! That is not to be." He sighed.

"I am of little use to you now and I have told your father, the great king Lir, that I will not be coming to the shore anymore. This is the last time that you will set eyes on old Mechair. I want to lay my tired hands on your foreheads for the last time and to hear just one song to take with me to the place of the long sleep. Please forgive me children!"

"Oh Mechair! Mechair our most trusted companion and friend. What will we do without you? It was you and father that made our punishment all that easier to bear. We will sing for you, here keep this and remember us." Fionnuala plucked a feather from her long wing and swam with it in her beak to him. Mechair took her into his arms and hugged her. The three brothers each plucked a feather and swam in turn to bid goodbye to him.

Mechair with tears streaming down his sad eyes hobbled from the shore. He climbed the well-worn path and leaning on his stick waved with the feathers to the children. Then he heard them sing a lament, as he had never heard it sung before. He waited, his heart breaking until the last cord died away across the lake. Kissing the feathers he left the lake for the last time. With Mechair now gone to the place of the long sleep there were few left that the swans really knew.

They watched as the royal servants brought their father down to the shore. He could no longer walk but he was determined that he would not go to the long sleep until the day of their departure.

70

One morning as they waited for their father to arrive, Fionnuala felt an urge to leave this place. She was the eldest and would be the first to feel the power of the spell.

The royal guards brought their father to the lakeshore and left him sitting with his children. His eyesight was so poor that he could not tell one of his children from the other. He had to rely on his sense of hearing.

They did not sing to him but began to talk about their mother Niamh and to thank him and the royal household for all the good times they had on the lake. Their father knew that it was now time for them to depart. There was a great sadness in his aching heart. He said little but listened to all that they had to say. Then there was silence for a moment. Tears welled up in his sad eyes and he wept unashamedly.

"Father! It is I, Aedh. I will never be king of the Tuathan-de-Dannan. I wish that I could have been but that was taken away from me. I know that I could never be as wise a king as you. You could not have done any more for us than you already have. What I am telling you, father, is that your vigil is past! You have done all that could be expected of a father and more. You need suffer no more. Go and be reunited with our mother Niamh. Give her our love and tell her that we will always love her. Go for the long sleep now father. Go! For we must leave the lake this morning and go to the cruel Straits of Moyle. Think of us, father in your long sleep. Think of the children of the lake." Each child plucked a special feather of down from their breasts and gave them to him.

"Did I not watch and care for you, for the last three hundred years and more. Is not the kingdom of Lir coming to an end? I only wish that I could fly with you to the cruel Straits of Moyle and watch over you. I knew that to day was the day of your departure. I have already made preparations for my long sleep beside my queen. your mother. I will sit here and listen as you fly away, my children. I will not see you ever again until we meet in Tír-na-nÓg. I will hear your song and I will send my best eagles to watch over you and protect you on your long journey. The beacons of the kingdom will be lit to guide you. Farewell my children!

"Oh father! We do not wish to leave you, but the spell draws so near." Aedh cried.

71

"We must go now." Fionnuala felt the curse and the pain of departure willing her to leave at once.

"If only that I could find some way to reverse the evil spell then you know I would. I am now the last king of the Tuathan-de-Dannan and from this day our mortal world will be no more."

"It is time my bothers, we must fly to the Straits of Moyle." Fionnuala called to the twins who were clinging to their father in the hope of staying. But stay they could not, they had to leave.

Aedh led his brothers and sister out on to the centre of the lake for the last time. He looked around him and with a sigh began to paddle across the lake then with a swish from his great wings he rose up into the morning sky. Looking behind him he saw his sister Fionnuala, close behind and she encouraging the twins. They rose in a straight line and began to circle the palace and their land, 'Tír-na-nÓg.

Six great eagles appeared in the sky over them. They were to be their bodyguards on their long journey to the Straits of Moyle.

They began to sing and their song echoed across the water of the lake. The people came from the palace, they cheered, they waved and they cried. Their father stood up, perhaps for the last time and faced where the music was coming from. He waved and waved until the last echo of their song faded. The lake was now empty and of no more interest.

Back at the lakeshore King Lir called on his guards to take him back to the palace. He would now go to the place of the long sleep.

Fionnuala took over the lead from Aedh as they flew north and on to the terrible Straits of Moyle. On over the land of Tír-na-nÓg they flew and at each kingdom they swooped low and sang to the people for the last time. Once again the people waved and cried. They knew that this would be the last time that they would see or hear the Children of Lir.

As they came to the last outcrop of their land one of the great eagles swept down from the sky and flew alongside them.

"We must turn back now, for we could not survive in the harsh climate of the Straits of Moyle. We have asked the Gods of the seas to visit you whenever they can. Fare well, fare well! 'Children of the great God Lir'. With a great sweep of his wings he and the other eagles swooped over the swans in a final salute. Then rising high above the children they returned to Tír-na-nÓg.

72

On through the icy rain and cold winds the children flew. The twins became frightened and began to cry.

"Have courage, little ones." Fionnuala seeing them being driven off course called.

"Aedh! Take over the leadership, I will fly alongside the twins and shelter them from the storm." She instructed. On, on they flew and the journey seemed to have no ending.

Looking down through the storm Aedh saw the barren wind swept rocks and the boiling seas. Then a chilly foreboding came over him as he felt the pull of the spell taking effect.

"These are the terrible Straits of Moyle. It is the place where we must spend the next three hundred years." Aedh looked back at Fionnuala. She did not need telling for she too had felt the pulling power of the spell.

The night sky was as black as the caves of the demons and the seas boiled. This was indeed a foreboding place.

Aedh saw a break in the storm and swooping down he landed in a sea of choppy ice. He called on his sister and the twins to land now lest they lose each other.

Conn landed with a splash and collided with a large boulder. Blood flowed from a gaping wound in his neck. Salt from the sea entered the wound and increased the pain. Fionnuala seeing his distress rushed to his side and helped him to he shelter of an outcrop of rocks.

"Don't worry little brother, I will soon make it better." She placed her wing around him and comforted him. Conn placed his neck deep within the down feathers of his sister and soon succumbed to a fitful sleep.

They spent the night huddled together on the sparse rocky outcrop. In keeping with the curse they were not allowed to shelter from the severe environment. They were so tired that they had little interest as to where they were. All they wanted to do for now was to rest.

Next morning they set about building a safe haven from stones, seaweed and seashells. They planned that if they were separated at any time then they would return to the haven. If any were lost at sea then they would sing and call until they found each other.

At the end of the first week they were to experience their first fierce storm. They clung to each other as the seas boiled and began to lash their haven. Fionnuala in accordance with the wishes of her father

73

tried to shelter the twins under her great wings. Then a mighty wave rose from the depths of the sea and swept them off the rock. Lightening flashed and thunder crashed across the vast open seas. Fionnuala came to the surface spluttering as she tried to disgorge the vile salt water. She shook herself and looked around her.

Where were the other children? They were now separated. She called but the noise of the clashing waves drowned her calls. The others too were calling for each other. All was in vain. Fionnuala worried for the twins. Were they together or had the storm separated them?

Fionnuala scrambled on to the comparative safety of an outcrop of slippery rocks. She tried to call but she was too exhausted. She was bitterly cold and all her strength had gone.

"Am I the last of the children of Lir, left alone in an empty ocean?" She questioned. She tried to remain awake and alert but slowly her long neck rested back on her body. Fionnuala was sleeping a fitful sleep.

She awoke cold and weary to a grey morning light. The storm had abated but the cold was intense. Rising she slipped into the cold ocean and was soon surrounded by ice flows.

Ignoring her own situation she swam on and on, calling. Calling and singing over the noise of the waves and the crashing foam. Blocks of ice hit her on the body and neck. Blood poured from her wounds. The salt of the seas bit deep into her open wounds but still her duty and instinct forced her to continue calling. She searched the ocean for some food to sustain herself. There was little to be found. By nightfall she could go no further and laying her head across her body, she left the seas buffet her battered body.

She knew that neither she nor her brothers could die. She wished that the Gods would show their pity and take them to the long sleep, but it was not to be. They would have to suffer from the cruel spell woven around them.

"If only they could be together to share their cruel dilemma." She thought

Waking she raised her head and saw that she was drifting back towards the haven. Then she remembered their promise to return to the haven should they ever be separated.

Through the icy swell she slowly drifted, her voice now mute from all the salt water she had swallowed. Her eyes were dimmed with the ice that was forming from her tears.

With her senses numbed she swam on towards the outcrop of rocks that was their sole haven. She was hungry but there was little food to be had in the Straits of Moyle.

"Perhaps my brothers are there waiting for me?" She took courage from her thoughts.

Then she heard a duet singing the songs of the Tuatan-de-Dannan.

With renewed strength she rose from the sea and flew to where she had heard the singing. She was overjoyed when she saw Aedh accompanied by Conn swimming slowly towards her. Aedh had a comforting wing around his younger brother; she was pleased to see such brotherly love. Swooping down she joined them on the surface of the ocean.

"Have you had any sightings of Fiacra?" Aedh asked.

"None! None at all, I have searched the oceans day and night." Too exhausted to search further the three swans returned to the haven and settled down for the night.

That night as they slept, Fionnuala had a dream. In it her mother, Queen Niamh came and spoke to her.

"You must rise and rescue your brother Fiacra. He is all alone and frightened in the cave of a thousand demons." She told her.

"I know not of this cave, how will I find it?" Fionnuala cried out in her sleep.

"You will find it, for you of the Tuatan-de-Dannan and the daughter of King Lir." Her mother spoke.

Fionnuala woke with a start, it was now dawn. She looked towards her sleeping brothers. Slowly she waddled towards Aedh and called gently to him.

"I know where Fiacra is, Aedh! Mother came to me in a dream and told me."

"We will go and find him now, let Conn sleep." Aedh looked up at the black sky hoping against hope that the weather might be kind to them. Alas it was not to be, icy snow driven by high winds obliterated the skyline. Freezing rain that had turned to icy daggers penetrated their feathers and inflicted cruel wounds to their bodies.

"What if he awakes and finds us gone?" Fionnuala who winched at every cruel dart that struck her, asked. She too looked at the foreboding weather.

"He will not awaken for some time. He is too exhausted by all the trauma." Aedh informed her.

They swam out to where the sea was free of ice. Paddling their feet and flapping their wings they were soon airborne.

"We must hurry Aedh, for the weather is closing in." She called as they battled against the great north winds.

After a long exhausting struggle against all odds Fionnuala had a premonition that the cave of the thousand demons was below the cloud cover.

Fionnuala swooped down and there on a craggy rock face she saw the cave and landed on the sea. Aedh landed soon after and they both began to swim towards the entrance. At the mouth of the cave they stopped and listened. Mourning winds echoed through the foreboding caves and made them shiver. Fionnuala started singing.

Aedh joined her in a duet. They sang and they sang, there was no response.

"Are you sure that this is the cave, Fionnuala?" Aedh asked.

"This is indeed the cave of a thousand demons. For did not the queen, our mother tell me so?"

Soon a weak voice from within the cave was heard to sing the song in reply.

"He is inside, we must rescue him at once." Aedh was about to enter the cave when he saw Fiacra come out from the dark interior.

"Are you able to fly, Fiacra?" Aedh asked.

"Yes! I think so, I am so glad to see you both. I spent the night hiding from the demons. It is safe now for they sleep by day and will not be active until nightfall. Where is Conn, is he not with you?"

"He is safe at the haven, come we must hurry back before he awakens and gets worried." Fionnuala flapped her huge wings in preparation for the long flight.

Fiacra was too weak from cold and hunger to take to the wing. Fionnuala had to warm him under her wing before he could fly. Aedh went out into the ice flows and diving deep below the waters found a

76

little food, which he fed to his brother. With Fiacra now refreshed the three swans rose high into the sky and returned the their haven.

One night the moon rose over the seas like a huge golden ball. Its light reflecting on the now still waters. The cold was so intense that they could hear the ice crackling on the surface. The children formed a tight circle close to each other to keep out the intense cold. The twins as usual were placed as near to the centre as possible and protected by the huge wings of Fionnuala and Aedh. Next morning Aedh noticed that Conn was no longer with them.

He tried to move from the rock but was unable . He was held captive by ice, which had formed around his feet as he slept. His brother and sister were in the same predicament. Shaking the frost from his wings he called Fionnuala and told her the sad news. She removed her wing from around Fiacra and in doing so awakened him.

"Fiacra! Your twin has gone missing during the night. We want you to stay here. You must not leave under any circumstances." Fionnuala warned him.

"What if you don't come back?" Fiacra looked concerned.

"Don't worry we will be back and so will Conn." Aedh assured him.

They dipped their great wings into the foam and spread it around their trapped feet until the ice melted and released them.

The two great birds rose up into the sultry sky. They spent most of the morning cries crossing each other over the seas in their search for their brother Conn.

Aedh heard Fionnuala singing and making a circle in the sky flew to where she was circling.

Below he saw Conn trapped in a block of drifting ice being buffeted by the sea.

"Don't worry Conn! We will soon have you back in the haven." He called as he swooped out of the sky and landed beside his brother.

Aedh and Fionnuala took up their stations on each side of the ice flow and pushed it all the way towards the haven. On the way the ice began to melt and soon Conn was free.

"Now Conn let us fly back to the haven, for your brother will be worried." Aedh encouraged his younger brother.

On reaching their shelter they circled and called as Fiacra watched with joy their safe return.

The children continued to suffer cruelly in the Straits of Moyle. Yet there were many adventures, which were not so hazardous. The whales and dolphins would come and visit them periodically on their migratory routes to the southern oceans. There was the time when several shoals of dolphins and whales all came at once.

"We heard you singing on our migratory route and have come to see you." A great white whale told them.

They told them that they had been asked by the great King Lir to call and see them whenever they could.

"How is our father? We thought that he had gone for the long sleep." The children asked.

"The great King Lir was given the magic by the druid Dal to come and visit us. This he requested as a last wish before the long sleep. It was on this final visit that he instructed us to come to this barren place and comfort you. We asked him if he had any message for you."

"There are no messages for my children. We said our last farewells on Lough Derryvaragh." He told us.

"It is so very lonely round the Straits of Moyle. We never visit this place." A female dolphin told them.

The whales and dolphins stayed for as long as they could but they too had to move south. They could not endure the cold and harsh conditions in the Straits of Moyle. To stay would mean death to them. Before they left they gave the children several shoals of fish to keep the hunger at bay.

"We would love to stay longer but the ice is closing in and we must return to the southern oceans." The whales and dolphins apologised.

During their short stays they told the children of the warm waters of the southern ocean and the green islands filled with singing birds and playful animals.

The children listened to their stories and when the time came for the whales and dolphins to leave, they remembered and they were sad. Once again they would be left alone in the empty cold seas in the Straits of Moyle. There would be no escape for them. The spell would have to run its span of three hundred years. Their suffering could not however last forever.

Final Chapter.

Ffinnuala sat on a rock close to the haven and watched as her brothers tried to catch a little food. Hunger was one of their great problems, that and the cold made life miserable for them.

As she contemplated on their miserable situation she felt the urge to flee from this barren and forsaken place. She stretched her wings as she felt the magic of the Tuatan-de-Dannan calling them home, their three hundred years imprisonment were at an end. Hooping and flapping her great wings in great agitation and joy she called on her brothers to abandon their search.

"The time has finally come! It is now that we can leave this horrible place." She flapped her wings and flew into the air.

Her brother abandoned their search for food and with a great hooping cry of relief and joy they rose high into the sky. The wild winds and the icy air no longer held them in dread. Setting their course south to the land of Tír-na-nÓg, they left the Straits of Moyle forever.

Higher and higher they flew and soon they felt the warm terminals of the southern seas. Aedh pointed ahead of them and began to sing. The others in their joy joined in the singing. They were now over the land of their birth. The fields were green and the mountains were covered in trees. Their joy knew no bounds as singing and swooping they flew on and on towards the kingdom of Lir and home.

They tried to locate the kingdoms of the Chieftains but could find no trace of them. They continued however to sing and sweep the great horizon, there was nobody to greet them.

When they finally reached the shore of lake Derryvaragh, they saw the ruins of their great palace. The place was over grown and of the Tuatan-de-Dannan kingdom there was no sign. Swooping down they landed in the ruins and began to call for their father. Their sorrow was all the more painful for the Tuatan-de- Dannan were no more. The kingdom was as silent as the great Dolmens. They began to sing a lament to the passing of their race.

That night they rested in the ruins of the palace. As the dawn awakened over the Irish sky they took to the wing once again and flew on to Sidhe Fionna and Inis Gloria as the spell demanded.

"Whatever has happened to our land?" Finnuala asked Aedh.

*"Don't you realise that we have been away a long time Fionnuala.
Remember what father said at the lakeside? He told us that it was the
last days of the kingdom of the Tuatan-de-Dannan."*

*When they reached the great Lough Dearg, they were surprised that
there too life had become extinct. The palace had gone and so had the
people. They had all gone to the great sleep long, long ago.*

*Next morning they sent Aedh out to Inis Gloria to seek a sanctuary for
them.*

*Aedh flew over the countryside and was soon circling the lake. As he
swooped down he noticed a smaller lake some distance away. It was
an ideal sanctuary. As the lake was fed from the waters from Inis
Gloria it was, for the carrying out of the spell the same waters.*

*Aedh returned and was delighted to tell them that he had at last found
a safe haven in the waters near to Inis Gloria.*

*"Is it really safe?" The twins pressed for assurances. They
remembered the harsh treatment they suffered on the Straits of Moyle.*

*"It is indeed safe, the waters are blue and calm and the banks are
filled with trees and singing birds. Come let us fly to it now."*

*Once again the children were on the wing to serve the last of their
trials and tribulations. When the others saw the place they had to
agree with Aedh. It was indeed a paradise.*

*"It must be the most beautiful lake in Tír-na-nÓg." Declared
Fionnuala.*

*Soon the children had created a haven suitable to their needs. Time
passed slowly on the leisurely lake. They spent most of their days
singing as they moved gracefully in the clear crystal waters.*

*Then one morning their tranquillity was disturbed by the arrival of an
old man with a beard. The children mistakenly thought that he was a
druid. As they were not too sure they kept their distance.*

*He immediately started to cut down some of the trees and began to
build a home. He collected stones and these he put in place between
the wooden uprights and daubed them with a mixture of mud and
reeds. The children watched as daily the structure took shape. It was
not like a house as they knew it. The old man was building a long
slender tower at one end.*

*Curiosity getting the better of them they began to move closer to the
shore. It was not too long before they had established a close*

relationship with the old man. The old man began to feed them pieces of bread. In the evening when he had finished his task for the day he would sit on the bank learning their songs and listening their beautiful music.

Curiosity getting the better of her, Fionnuala decided that she would find out what this stranger was doing at the side of their remote lake. Cautiously she came nearer and nearer to where the old man was daubing his house with mud.

"Tell me! Are you one of our druids from Tír-na-nÓg?" She asked. The old man was surprised to hear a swan talking. They had never spoken to him before. In his surprise he fell into the water.

"Was that you speaking to me?" Rising from the water he looked deep into Fionnuala's eyes.

"Yes! Sorry I surprised you. I asked are you a Druid?"

"No I am not a druid. They vanished from Erin many, many years ago. Why do you ask?

"We! That is my brothers and I are the children of King Lir. We are descendants of the druids. We are the race of the Tuathan-de-Dannan from Tír-na-nÓg."

"I heard of you in the old Sean Sceals of Erin." By now the three brothers seeing that Fionnualla was getting on so well with the old man came and joined them.

"Are you one of the Holy men that we were told about so very long ago?" Fiacra questioned him.

"I am indeed what you say, I am a holy man. A disciple of St Patrick. We are followers of the lord and master."

"The lord and master, who might he be?" Conn asked.

"The Lord and master is Jesus Christ and we are his followers."

"We! There is but one of you?" Aedh looked puzzled at the old man.

"We are many and are growing by the hour. Have you never heard of us? Sorry! I forgot that you are the children of Lir. You would not have heard of us of course." He apologised.

"We may not have heard of you but that does not mean that we would not like to. Our wicked stepmother told us that one-day holy men would come to Tír-na-nÓg. They would ring a bell and when they did then the spell on us would be broken."

"On this spot I am building my church and I will be putting a bell in the belfry. That is the long spire that you see. I will teach you all *about my lord and master, Jesus Christ if you so wish. By the way my name is Ceamhoch."*

Ceamhoch spent many years at the lakeside teaching the children and in return listening to their stories and songs. He would leave the lakeside for long periods and when he returned he would have a bag with him containing iron ore. This he would put into a large pot. One day he told the swans that he now had enough metal to make a bell. He would now build a furnace and make a mould. The pieces of metal he would melt down and pour into the mould.

The children did not understand what it was all about. They did understand that should he succeed in making the bell and ringing it, then the spell may be broken.

Ceamhoch made his bell and when it cooled he knocked it out of its mould. The children watched fascinated and anxious. Next morning the children were at the lakeshore bright and early. The holy man came from his hut and attached a rope to the bell holder and hung it in his belfry. The swans followed him into the church.

He blessed his bell and dedicated it to the children of Lir and the blessed Trinity. As he was about to take the rope in his hands and ring the bell the door was flung open.

Armed soldiers entered the church and took up aggressive positions. Drawing their swords they faced the hermit.

"What do you people want? This is the house of the Lord. You must not bring weapons inside." Ceamhoch rose and challenged the intruders.

"We have come to take them away." The leader drew his broad sword and pointed it at the four swans.

"No! You cannot take them. This is the house of the Lord. Sheath your swords in the name of Jesus Christ." The hermit demanded.

The soldier ignoring the protests of the holy man stepped forward and placed the point of his sword under Ceamhoch's chin in a threatening manner.

I am Lairgneanen, King of Connaught. My wife, Deichthe, who is a princess of Munster heard of the singing swans. I promised her that she should have them and have them she will." Lairgneanen demanded.

"Then you will have to kill me first." Ceamhoch spread out his arms in front of the swans to protect them.

82

"If you do not move away I will kill you and burn your so called church to the ground." Lairgneanen was now really angry.

The children were now getting excited for they knew that the spell was about to be broken. The spell had finally come full circle as foretold.

Fionnuala rose up to her full height and challenged the great king.

"We are the children of King Lir, we will not allow you to harm this innocent man." Her brothers came to her side and opening their great white wings stood guard over the holy man.

The King looked with amazement at the swans. Not alone could they sing but they could speak as well. What a wonderful present they would make for his wife, he thought.

He called on his men to kill Ceamhoch and take the birds to the wicker cages in the cart outside the church. The soldiers fearful of the magic of the holy man did not kill him but pushed him roughly to one side. Then four of the soldiers picked up the swans and took them towards the cages.

Ceamhoch saw his opportunity, rising to his feet he ran towards the rope.

Clang! Clang! The holy bell tolled for the first time.

All at once the feathers began to fall from the swans. The soldiers dropped the swans on to the ground and looked in amazement. Before the assembly laid three men and a woman, all were very, very old. Four crippled, wizened and haggard people rose feebly from the ground. Fionnuala approached the startled soldiers and opening her arms wide declared...

"We are the Children of King Lir. Ruler of Tír-na-nÓg." She stood proud and defiant before the king and proclaimed their ownership of Tír-na-nÓg.

The king on seeing the old people standing before him and thinking that they would bewitch him ran in terror from the church. Turning his back on the lake he left them in peace, never to return.

The children lived with Ceamhoch by the shore of the lake for many years and he converted them to Christianity. After eight years Ceamhoch died and the children buried him in the grounds surrounding the little chapel. They rang the bell in his memory and sang a sad lament. The spell had now come full cycle.

They too were growing tired and longed for the place of the long sleep. They wanted to be joined once again with their father and mother. Who was there left to show them the place of the long sleep? Their ravaged bodies ached with pain and they found it hard to catch any food.

"Are we to be denied the long sleep?" Conn pleaded one day as he staggered into the little chapel.

"Be patient little brother, and this goes for us all. Remember Niamh, our mother and our father the great king Lir. They have not forgotten the children of Lir. They will come and take us to the long sleep when the time is right." Fionuuala assured her brothers.

One night as Fionnuala slept her mother again visited her.

"You will suffer no more my children. The spell is past, your father King Lir and I await your return. I have come to take you to the place of the long sleep. You will suffer no more. To morrow as the noon sun sits in the sky I will show you the way." With these words her mother faded from her dreaming.

Next morning Fionnuala called her brothers to her side and told them of the dream.

"To day at noon we must be brave and strong for we must swim to the centre of the lake and await the arrival of our mother." She told them.

"But we are old and will not be able to swim to the centre of the lake." Fiacra was worried; he felt that it was an impossible task for them to perform.

"We are the last of the Tuatan-de-Dannan to walk on talab na h-Éireann and we are the children of Lir, no task is beyond our capability. Aedh boasted.

They set about making preparations for the long journey, there was little time left. In fear and trepidation they entered the lake for the last time. They swam to the centre of the lake and forming a tight circle began to sing.

The sun rose in the sky and sent long shadows over the lake. As the sun rose higher the shadows grew shorter. Still the children sang louder. Then there were no more shadows for it was now noon.

The shadows began to form again but the music has ceased. Of the children of Lir there was no trace. The curse inflicted on the innocent children of King Lir on lough Derryvaragh came full circle on the waters of Lake Gloria.

P.S. The story is told that a long boat was seen leaving the lake carrying the bodies of the children of Lir. It entered the river Shannon sailing south to Lough Dearg. From there it crossed to the long resting place deep beneath the Kingdom of Ainy at Lough Gur. It is said by many that they often hear the children of Lir singing on the vast Lough Derg in the cool of the evening to this day.

It is believed in Ireland that the souls of virgins are enshrined in white swans and any mortal who entraps or kills them will die within twelve months and a day.

The story is told of a prosperous landlord in Munster who had eleven swans put to death for eating his salmon fry. Shortly afterwards his wife and eleven children were drowned on Lough Dearg. A great misfortune came upon his lands and he too died.

Are we sure? Do we know? Did you hear the children singing on Lough Dearg?

THE OLD WARRIOR

'I met a beggar on my way,
"Good day to you." To me he said.
His form bent, his hair was grey,
He reeked so foul I could not stay.

He greeted me, I knew not why?
Ignoring his greeting I passed him by:
Keeping my distance I diverted my eyes,
Avaunt! I sighed then I heard him sigh.

Rusting medals pinned to his breast,
Decaying in tatters his regimental crest?
Reaching the ridge I looked back on him,
His eyes were tearful, dreamy and dim.

I felt ashamed and humbly thought:
'How many wars had this soldier fought?'
I raised my hand and saluted him,
A humble gesture for my selfish sin?'

LOUIE BYRNE©

86

THE OUTCAST

I am of your kin, what was my sin?
Was it my bride I sought to win?
She had no wealth, no gold in store,
That's why I loved her all the more.

Why did you pass us in the street?
In lane or park would you us greet?
You'd look through us, I dare to say?
Just as if we weren't there.

You never looked us in the face,
Although we're of your kin and race.
Because I wed beneath your taste,
You think that I'm a real disgrace.'

Little need now for your tears,
To meet us more you need not fear.
My Mary's gone, there's no tomorrow,
I laid her down in grief and sorrow.

Now I'm the one with head held high,
I'll walk the streets and pass you by.
Troubled conscious, you'll find not rest,
For empty pride is all you've left.

LOUIE BYRNE©

87

BROKEN HEARTED

Life's like an actor in a play;
For actors thoughts they cannot say.
Though they act they cannot stay,
At curtain call they fade away.

Ghostly figures come on the scene,
They dance, they romp with abandoned glee.
Like mermaids in a sea of green,
From mortal eyes they vanish when seen.

Life is filled with ups and downs,
Our dreams, our hopes, cross-furrowed brows.
It's all an act, as the curtain falls?
Or our last chance an accolade to call?

The lights grow dim I wipe my brow,
'I've taken now my final bow,
Adieu! Adieu good friends!
No use pretending, for me this is the end.'

LOUIE BYRNE©.

A CASE OF MISTAKEN IDENTITY

'Ah vain are you who will not say,
"Come in good friend, why don't you stay.
To share good cheer, you're welcome here."
Alas! Your heart is cold, in selfish fear,
In bitter spite you're growing old,
What friends you had, they are no more.'
Vanity Louie Byrne©

"Will you look at him, staggering down the road. The worst for drink and at this time of the morning too, should be ashamed of himself?" The two women watched old Alfie staggering along the high road in Thomondgate in Limerick. In his hand he held a plastic shopping bag. Peeping out from the top was the tell tale label from a bottle of Guinness stout.

"Sure that's Alfie from across the lane, no better and no worse than most. Never knew him to touch a drop, God help the poor soul. Wonder where he goes to every day with his bit of shopping?"

"Never touch a drop did you say, did you not see the bag? Bottles of porter and whiskey, if you don't be minding. Where he gets all the money from, I'd like know? Did you see the gait of him the ould drunkard?" Mary tightened her shawl round her.

"Don't exaggerate Mary, it's only one small bottle. Sure he only walks like that because there's something wrong with his hips." Brige, her companion looked sympathetically after Alfie.

"You're too kind with your sympathy Brige, so you are. You'll get your reward in Heaven, no doubt." Mary chided her.

"Not at all Mary, sure the truth never hurt anyone. Now did it, speak fair?"

"Have it your way, I'll not argue with you. Come on or we'll miss the bus." Both women on seeing the bus climbing the hill hurried towards the bus stop. As they crossed the street they heard the screech of brakes and then the bang.

"Jesus, Mary and Joseph whatever were that?" Brige blessed herself and looked out from her black shawl.

89

"There's been an accident, the bus hit something. Another coss (Stray dog) no doubt!" Both women hurried to where the bus had slid to an emergency halt.

"Oh God help us, the poor old soul, is he dead?" Brige removed her shawl and falling to her knees began to pray.

"Did any of you see what happened, please?" The driver in an agitated state jumped down from the cab and appealed to the gathering crowd. Under the front nearside wheel lay the crushed head of Alfie. His body was half on the pavement and half in the gutter. There was no mistake by the amount of blood on the road but that he was dead.

"I saw it all, don't blame yourself son. I was telling Brige here a minute ago about that drunkard, wasn't I Brige? God be good to his soul. Can't you smell the drink and see it with your own two eyes." Mary pointed to the broken bottles lying on the road. The contents mixed with Alfie's blood as it trickled slowly down the gully. A small loaf, a tin of beans and a small woodbine were scattered along the roadside.

"Mary, that's an awful thing to say, how could you have seen what happened and we halfway down the street?" Brige rose from her knees and interrupted.

"Sure wasn't he staggering along the road when we passed him and he smelling like a brewery? Can you deny it?" Mary retorted.

"He was no such thing, you should be ashamed of yourself talking about the dead like that. May God forgive you, Mary Culligan? Here's the guards now let them deal with it." A police car with its blue light flashing and siren wailing came to a halt behind the bus. Two guards rushed from the car.

"Stand back the lot of you." One of the guards pushed the crowd back as the other went and inspected the body.

"He's gone John, God rest his soul. Call for an ambulance." The guard challenged his fellow officer as he removed his cap out of respect.

"Any of you see what happened here?" One of the guards removed his notebook and studied the gathering.

"I did guard, this drunkard...' Mary in an agitated state came forward.

90

"Steady on now Mam, there's no need to insult the poor man's memory, God be good to him. Don't jump to conclusions. Just tell me what you saw and where you were at the time." The guard tried to calm the agitated woman.

"I was up there right at the brow of the hill when I heard the bang and saw the drunken blackguard stagger into the path of the bus. Could have killed someone so he could. Sure the poor driver had no chance whatsoever." She confirmed.

"You were up there you say?" The guard pointed into the distance.

"I see, well you had best go down to the barracks and tell them all you saw. Will you do that now? Excuse me please. Anyone else see what happened, does anyone know his name?" The guard ignoring Mary looked to the gathering.

"You're not taking me seriously, Guard. Do you think I'd make it up or that I'm not telling you the truth?" Mary tugged at the guard's sleeve.

"His name is Alfie McQuaid and he lives over there on the Quarry Road. A harmless poor cratur, God be good to his soul. Suffered from some form of Epilepsy I believe." A bystander volunteered.

"Did you see what happened?" The guard asked.

"I doubt if anyone saw it, it was all over so quick. I wouldn't put any blame on the driver though; Alfie had a habit of falling over, it's his bad hip if you must know. I'd say that it was the will of the Almighty."

"Excuse me young man, what do you mean fall over. The man was drunk I tell you. Are you trying to take the sight out of my eyes? Sure the guards can see the evidence, broken bottles all over the road." Mary again interrupted.

"Will you shut your mouth woman, drunk indeed? There's one half pint Guinness bottle and a small quarter whiskey bottle. Stop jumping to conclusions and let the guards do their duty and keep your filthy remarks to yourself." The bystander looked with disgust at Mary.

"Will you go down to the barracks as I asked and let me deal with this gentleman?" The guard insisted. The ambulance came on the scene and following photographs and measurements of the road his body was removed and taken to the hospital morgue.

"Poor ould Alf! From what we know of him he was a loner. We'd often see him with a plastic bag filled with a little shopping. Where he was off to with it we never knew. At times he would purchase a small *packet of cigarettes although he was never known to smoke or drink. A man of mysteries, a loner I'd say but harmless. Kept himself to himself. Sorry I couldn't be more helpful." The bystander gave what information he had to the guard.*

"I can confirm that he was not drunk and from what you tell me that is likely what happened. He must have taken a dizzy spell and fell over. Poor ould soul. Do you know if he has anyone belonging to him?"

"Alf! I doubt it very much. I've lived here all my life and I've never seen anyone call to his door. He kept himself very much to himself, but I've already told you that."

In a little cottage in a laneway off Roxborough road old Dan Murrey looked anxiously from his sick bed towards the door.

'He's late, so he is. I badly need the bedpan. God! I hope nothing has happened to him. What would I do without his help? Alfie! What's keeping you old friend?' He thought as he numbered his beads.

Old Dan was incapacitated and could neither speak nor walk since a massive heart attack confined him to his bed. His only contact with the outside world was through Alfie his lifeline and long-standing friend. Dan had lost his wife the previous year to T.B. Neither he nor his wife had ever trusted banks and kept what money and valuables they possessed in a secure hiding place. Alfie was a gem solid as a rock, honest and a faithful companion. Faithful and reliable old Alfie would not let him down, like a well oiled clock he was. There had to be an excuse for his lateness.

His trust and faith in his old friend was such that he disclosed to him the hiding place of his savings and valuables before he became totally incapacitate. Alfie collected his pension every Thursday and placed it in the hiding place. Whenever shopping was needed Alfie would go to the secret hiding place and retrieve just enough money to pay for the goods.

Dan's only relative was a nephew and his wife living up country. Seldom did they call to see poor old Dan and his wife in the past. Now that he was totally incapacitated and badly needed their assistance they stopped visiting.

They were aware that uncle Dan; as they called him had a fair bit of money and valuables stashed away in some secret hiding place. They were anxious to get their hands on this but were reluctant to offer him any hospitality or assistance in return.

92

"It's about time you visited your uncle. He could drop dead any day and where would that leave us?" His wife reminded him one evening.

"You're right love, no use tempting providence. We'll go down this weekend and see how he's getting on. I'll remind him to settle his affairs when we're there. Wouldn't want him dying on us before he disclosed his hiding place, now would we? Hope he doesn't expect us to clean him and his house. Wonder what fool does it for him?" Her husband laughed.

"That smelly ould miser, wouldn't touch him with a barge pole. Sure what use has he for money anyway and he confined to his bed. Have a good look for his bank or savings book. He's bound to have one?" His wife gave a mock shiver...

"So you've come at last." Old Dan looked up from his bed and called out as the silhouette of Alfie appeared in the doorway.

"Sorry Dan, I broke the bottle on my way here but never mind I'm here now. Come on old pal, get out of that bed and let's away from here for we have more pleasant journeys to take and far nicer places to see." Reaching out his hand he encouraged Old Dan to rise from the bed and join him.

"Coming Alfie. I knew you wouldn't let me down, old mate." Dan now invigorated rose from his bed and followed his friend Alfie into the horizon.

His nephew and wife arrived at the cottage two days too late. They were shocked to see the wasted form of old Uncle Dan slumped across the bed his life long expired. They searched long and hard for his money and valuables but...?

Only Dan and Alfie know where they are hidden and they are not telling.

93

THE DRUNKARD'

In youth I shared a Christian cross,
A mother's love not to be forgot:
With other travellers unrefined,
My mother's love I soon resigned.

Abandoned Rosary that's never said,
They're mothers' beads above my bed.
They hang like tears on a lonely grave,
As in drunken stupor I rant and rave.

Drunken brawls and foremen swearing,
In gutters foul sometimes awaking.
A disgusting rake a handout seeking,
At Chapel door a vile wreck reeking.

The years rolled on in idle pleasure,
What time was left I ne're did measure.
Unopened letters in my mothers' hand,
Lay abandoned on the old hall-stand.

From drunken slumber I awakened,
My life a wreck, my friends forsaken.
Sick with shame and selfish sorrow,
Depressed, I saw passed life with horror.
Oh Mother! Mother can you not hear?
Your love I seek for death is near.
Reaching up, your beads I'm seeking,
My eyes grow dim; is that you speaking?

Louie Byrne©

94

CONFESSION

'What will I say when God I meet,
And humbly kneel before his seat?
Shall I relive the life I led?
And beg his mercy for tears I shed?

Then humbly shrink in my defeat,
To punishment unknown retreat:
Too late now to confess my sins,
The life I led and what has been.

For the life I led I now must pay,
Alone I stand; it's judgement day.
I seek not pity or humble prayers:
I plead by guilt, relief to gain.

In servitude to pay the price,
In hope of putting a wrong to right?
What am I thinking, what am I saying?
Is not for me my mother praying?'

LOUIE BYRNE©.

THE CAGED LINNET

'You who live in liberty and free,
Why did you snatch me from my tree?
My freedom took with gum and string:
In dungeons deep to hear me sing,
You think I sing for you in joy?
Do you not know it's my dying cry'?

A tinkling bell, a mirror swings,
On tiny chains for comfort bring.
Oh human! Are you so vain?
You think these gifts, my love you'll gain?
What was my crime to imprison me?
In a golden prison! Oh shame on thee.

Are you naive, or a sadistic being?
For love or vanity, did you bring me here?
A cuttle fish stuck in the bars;
A pinch of seed, a water jar.
A little gift, a lettuce leaf,
Are these rewards to ease my grief?

In the morning breeze I hear birds sing,
But little comfort to me they bring.
Set me free! Set me free I rant with rage,
For I'm a prisoner in a golden cage.
My wings are crippled from lack of flight,
My eyes are dimmed from glaring lights.

Would that God in mercy look?
And write my name in the golden book.
To take me from this prison hell,
From cuttlefish and tinkling bells.
To fly and sing was his holy will,

96

With obscene right this gift you killed?

'Oh think of me, once wild and free?
A prisoner now for all to see.
You call it love? That cannot be.
It's mental anguish can you not see?
As other birds the dawn do tell,
I am your prisoner in a metal hell!'

· *LOUIE BYRNE©*

THE LIMERICK PIG

They thought it strange when I a youth,
Took on the task a runt to brood.
They called you names, they were so rude,
They cast you out, they were so cruel.
'She'll never make it, why waste your time?'
With kicks and belts they said your mine.

I picked you up from the muddied green,
You did not squeal you were too weak.
I wiped you clean your wounds did heal,
You followed me through fallowed fields.
When others took their dogs for walks,
They looked at you, they laughed and talked.

The days the months they soon passed by,
You grew and grew into a fine fat sow.
With envious looks, regret and greed,
They took you from me that Christmas Eve.
Oh how I cried and pleaded too,
For you old friend I loved and knew.

'Fare thee well proud beast,
To strangers you are but a feast.
They hung you high, I heard you cry,
I looked not back but gave a sigh.
From bonabh to pig I watched you grow,
Your life they took, I'll say no more.'

LOUIE BYRNE©

MOLLY
THE LOST CAUSE

In sadistic delight the mob roar about,
Two gladiators ready to fight a bout.
The lights above the hall grow dim,
Like fighting cocks they're there to win.
They cheer they shout and goad them on,
Through blood and sweat he hears the bell.
The lights are up, the mob, they yell,
In dejected tears he clings to the rope,
Their thumbs are down, for him there's no hope.'

Lost cause. Louie. Byrne.

In the County of Donegal outside the twin towns of Ballybofey and Stranolar lived Michael and Rose Kelly. They were the proud owners of a small cottage and an acre of grassland. As the years rolled on they were blessed with a family of seven children. Times were not too good to them but then, as Michael would philosophically predict, 'God will provide Rose, you mark my word'. As they knelt to recite family rosary Michael would encourage them to plead to their God to bless them and to give them a little help. Not a lot just enough to see them through the hard times...

One day as he was walking round his small patch he heard a noise coming from the far corner of the field. Michael less audacious than most men but enamoured of the unknown blessed himself. Aware of the power of the leprechauns he cautiously crept towards the spot mindful of what may be lurking inside. Parting the branches he apprehensively peeped inside.

"Well bless my soul what have we here?" Before his eyes he saw a cow eating his grass, not that he minded in the least. Running toward the house as fast as his legs would carry him, he began calling to his wife.

"Rose! Rose will you come and see what I found?" He called.

"Whatever is the matter?" She called from the porch as their children gathered round her skirt wondering what their father was shouting about.

"Come and see for yourself?" He challenged.

"It's a cow, wherever did she come out of?" She looked down at the beast. The cow continued chewing the grass without raising her head.

99

The family stood gazing in at the cow unable to comprehend as to where she came from. The cow raised her head and taking a look at them in idle curiosity lay down and began chewing her cud. Her peace was slightly disturbed as the children shouted with joy.

"That's strange, hope she is not a fairy cow." Michael looked with apprehension at the beast.

"I'll fetch the water from the Doon well and sprinkle some on her as we say a prayer." Rose left the scene and returned with the holy water.

Having blessed the cow and the surrounding land they knelt and prayed. Content that this was no fairy gift they stroked her neck and spoke gently to her.

"Can we keep her, please Dad?" The children pleaded as they stroked and kissed the noble beast.

"Don't be silly now, that beast belongs to others. We must inform the guards at once." Their mother told them.

Time passed and the cow settled into the meadow. One day a guard came to the house bringing good news.

"Michael nobody has called to claim that cow, you may as well keep her."

"Keep her but I never kept a cow before?" Michael scratched his head.

"I wish I was as lucky as you, Michael. It's not often that one gets a cow for nothing. Think of all the milk you'll get for your children?"

Michael was now convinced that she was a gift from God himself.

Early each morning Rose went down the meadow accompanied by her children and milked the cow, now named Molly. After school as the shadows of night lengthened, the children would go down the meadow and sit with her. There they would maintain a dreamy silence broken now and then by the buzzing insects. Molly would waggle hers ears as one landed on her. The children would laugh and show their concern by shooing it off her. They were united in their welfare for Molly. She was patient and tolerant when the children played their imaginary games round her. When grass was scarce the children would take her along the roadside to partake of 'Gods acre' as the roadside grass verges were known. One day on returning from school they were surprised to see her down the field with a calf.

"Be careful now children and don't upset Molly and her baby." Their mother warned. There was little need for her to worry for Molly, seeing them charging down the field looked towards them with love and understanding. She knew that the children would love her baby as much as she did. Soon the calf was as mischievous as were the children. Their parents were happy with the situation for such ties of friendship could never be broken. Times however took a turn for the worst and although it broke the children's' hearts the calf had to be sold. Explaining the situation they found themselves in was left to their mother. Molly looked sorrowful as her calf was taken from the field against her will. She watched in sorrow as it was loaded into a cart and taken away. Much as they regretted selling the calf they were left with no alternative. When the cold hand of poverty knocks on ones door the best must be made of a bad situation. It would appear that Molly understood and accepted the situation for soon she settled back into her old routine.

One evening Michael sat in his local public house extolling the virtues of Molly and telling of the miracle in finding her. In a far corner sat a stranger quietly listening to all that was being said. Next morning as Rose returned with the bucket of milk the stranger was standing at the gate leading to the cottage waiting.

"Good morning, is there something that I can do for you?" She asked.

"Morning Mam. I understand that you came in possession of a stray cow some time ago?" He lifted his caubéen from his pole.

"We did that but when no one claimed her, she became ours."

"That cow belongs to me and I've come to collect her." He challenged.

"If the cow is yours; as you claim then by all means have her. Could the children say good bye to her before you take her?" Rose asked.

"Oh very well, but hurry it up." Grumbled the stranger.

The children came from the house and hearing that Molly was to be taken away burst into tears. They clung to her neck and covered her in kisses. They followed her down the laneway as the stranger pulled tightly on the rope.

"Please be gentle with our Molly." The children pleaded and cried on seeing the brutal way she was being treated.

"Get away home with you now?" Grumbled the indifferent stranger.

"Good bye Molly we'll always love you and remember you." They called and waved as she slowly disappeared into the distant hills. They listened in sorrow as her mournful 'Mooo' echo round the hills of Donegal.

"Molly is gone." Roses voice was choked with emotion as the related what happened to her husband on his return.

"Gone! Gone where?" Michael demanded to know.

"Dad! Will he be good to our Molly? Will we ever see her again?" The children pleaded and lamented.

"Don't worry children I'll go and tell the guards what happened." Michael took his old bicycle from the shed and took off to the town. The sergeant listened with sympathy to his story.

"Sorry Michael that was no owner. There has been a knocker here this last week buying cattle. I expect by now your cow is sold for slaughter."

"I daren't tell the children it would break their hearts." Michael replied.

"Hold on a minute, he didn't pay for her did he? That's stealing. Tell me what direction did the knocker take?" The sergeant asked.

"He took the Derry road, my wife told me." Michael ran his hand nervously round the rim of his caubeen.

"Hold on there a minute, get in the motor." The sergeant jumped into the drivers seat and set the car in motion. He stopped at the cottage and collected the family.

The sergeant drove the squad car at high speed towards the city of Derry...

Molly smelt the blood as she was led into the yard of a slaughter house and began to panic. She could not understand why her friends had deserted her and sent her to such a Hell. Forcing her into a small enclosure they tied her tightly to a metal fence.

"We'll slaughter this one next." The butcher wiping his bloodstained axe on his sack apron informed the knocker.

In deep despair she lay in the bloodied straw and accepted her fate. She was awakened with a kick and dragged to a ring set into the floor. She heard the slaughter man sharpen his axe on a grinding stone and knew that her end was near. She recalled the children's' friendship and the happiness she enjoyed in their company. She wished them well.

Resigned to her fate she hoped that her death would be painless and quick. 'If only I could have a last drink of water to relieve my thirst' she thought as the cruel chain throttled her. Her throat was parched and her eyes bloodshot. She thought she heard the children calling. She listened again but all was silent.

"Am I dreaming?" She thought. In her minds eye she saw them running down the old field somewhere near Ballybofey in the County Donegal to greet her. If only I could answer them she cried as tears welled up in her sad eyes.

"Molly! Molly where are you?" She heard them crying.

"No! This could not be. I must be dreaming? Please kill me now this is too much to bear." She was in deep distress from the cruel chains holding her head against the cold murdering block. Her breathing was impaired by her forced imprisonment on the stony ground. She saw the bloodied axe raised above her. Her heart raced. 'This is it.' She sighed. She closed her eyes as flashing lights passed through her brain- then all went black.

"Molly! Molly!" She heard the children call as she floated through hallucinatory consciousness again and again.

"It cannot be, what has happened?" She cried.

Again she thought that she heard the children. She wanted to call out but could not for her lungs were filled and the cruel chains muted her voice. They in turn could not hear her piteous lamentations as she choked. How she wished that she could let them know where she was. If only to say her last good-bye to them. No! She didn't want them to see her wallowing in her own blood. It would be too much for them to comprehend.

"What was the slaughter man waiting for? Why is he letting me suffer so much pain? Has the brute no pity? Get it over and done with here and now?" She pleaded. Suddenly the door was pushed open. She saw the axe fall to the ground beside her.

"Molly! Oh Molly what have they done to you?" The children cried. Choked with emotion Michael rushed forward and released her from her imprisonment.

"You're both under arrest, lucky for you that I stopped you killing that valuable beast." The sergeant fastened the handcuffs on to the wrists of the slaughter man and the knocker.

The children with a multitude of hands all trying to embrace Molly at the same time escorted her out of the slaughterhouse. They gave her a cool drink and washed her wounds clean.

"Come on old girl we're going home to Ballybofey." Michael gently called to her.

She was loaded into a horsebox together with fresh hay and a large bucket of fresh spring water. The children insisted that they too should travel with her.

Molly saw the gap of Barnesmore before her and smelt the sweet scent of heather. She let out a long 'Mooo.' Although tired from the trauma and fatigued she found renewed energy. Molly was home to where she belonged. Where she would be well treated and happy.

In time she gave birth to a fine second healthy calf. She knew that this one would not be leaving the homestead.

This was to be her destiny and needless to say she spent the remainder of her life chewing the cud and sharing the tenderness and gratitude of the children and their devoted parents in the wild hills of dear ould Donegal.

MINE ALONE

'I am but a living voice,
In hymn and prayer to God rejoice.
And when the bell of fate is tolled,
With fellow men I'll weep and moan.

On the pages of the golden book,
I pray past deeds you'll seek to look.
To fellow man I gave my trust,
And helped the needy as one must.

Here I stand at the Golden gate,
To wait my God, what is my fate?
There's no time left for a backward glance,
The burdens heavy, I must face the task.

I hope to reach the Promised Land,
And reaching out touch God's helping hand.
This is my wish, my hope to see,
Who would want to take this faith from me?'

LOUIE BYRNE©.

FOR LOVE OF ANGELENE

'That morning I remember,
Was in the month of December.
Angelene and I went to school together.
The air was crisp the ice was right:
It was my chance I held you tight.
My heart beat fast but it couldn't last,
For the clock told me I'd be late for class.'

Yet I was patient and I could wait,
As homeward bound we stopped at the gate.
I whispered that my love was true,
You told me then that so was yours.
I stroked your hair so soft and fair,
Then a voice rang out in the evening air,
'Get away from here, get from my gate'.

That evening I came down your street,
Perhaps with you I there would meet.
Beneath a lamplight I stood and shivered,
'Twas not the cold that made me diddle.
At last you came and we embraced,
We kissed and cuddled and our hearts did race,
Until your mother came through the gate.

LOUIE BYRNE©.

106

THE HUMBLE SERVANT

'Why in life did they not show,
Their gratitude, a smile or more?
Or show how much I meant to them.
To meet the task that I was sent?

How much their thanks would mean to me,
A little gratitude, for what had been?
Yet ignored was I and treated badly,
Starved and beaten I cried sadly.

To serve them well that was my task,
Food and shelter was all I asked.
The heavy wheel fell from the rim,
Trapped and alone the light grew dim.

Excruciating pain in anguish raved,
To free me from this captive grail.
I cannot feel the pain no more,
Shadows come they call me home.

Serene I leave the tragic scene,
I'm free and equal, a mystic being.
No humble servant. Now proud and free?
No more to toil, no longer seen.

LOUIE BYRNE©

THE SULLEN REAPER

With scabbards bare and baying dogs,
They trapped the felon in open bog.
I am no slave for a foreign crown,
The sullen reaper cried when brought to ground.

With whip and dog they chastised him,
They dragged him to an iron rim.
With chains and ropes they did insist,
The sullen reaper that did resist.

They shackled him and put him down,
Revolt you cur against the crown.
You'll pay for this you freedom seeker,
They spat at him the sullen reaper.

When evening came they cut him loose,
Then o'er a tree they cast a noose.
This is a lesson from me your keeper,
The Redcoat screamed at the sullen reaper.

Then round his neck they placed the noose,
And from his feet removed his boots.
The time has come to meet your keeper,
They laughed and hanged the sullen reaper.

LOUIE BYRNE©.

THE BOOK OF KELLS

How long more, the question was asked?
As the happy monks worked on their task.
When God made time, he thought of us,
His humble scholars, replied the monks.

The years rolled on and took their toll;
The happy scribblers were growing old.
As what it contains we'd like a look?
The abbot pleaded as his seat he took.

To show it now would be a sin.
The monks replied with a wayward grin.
"You must be patient, pray awhile."
With cheek in jowl at the abbot smiled.

We're growing anxious the book to read.
To see what's written it isn't greed.
And then one day at the sound of the bell,
The monks disclosed 'The Book Of Kells.'

LOUIE BYRNE©.

THE DANCING SHOES

The Abandoned Greyhound.
You treated me with dreadful scorn,
Forgetting that a rose has thorns.
You told me that new love you found,
Too old you said to hunt new grounds.
My gait is slow, my eyes are dim,
But a faithful companion I've always been.
You leave the house with a brindled bitch,
My home is now beneath a ditch.
My coat is ragged my feet are sore,
I beg my food from open doors.
Remember the days when fleet of foot?
I filled your cabinet with silver cups?

Louie Byrne©

Mary Ryan climbed the small hillock behind her fathers' cottage and sat on the green sward. Locking her hands round her knees she looked into the horizon.

"Dreaming of me were you?" Pat Slattery, her childhood sweetheart crept up behind her.

"Don't do that Pat, you frightened the life out of me." She chided him as he sat down beside her and kissed her.

"The builders will be starting on the house soon. I hope it's finished before our wedding." He informed her.

"Wouldn't it be wonderful to spend our wedding night in a caravan like the travellers down there do?" She looked down at a caravan situated at the side of the road.

"Not likely Mary. Did I tell you, there's a meeting in the rambling house this coming Saturday. You'll come of course?" He informed her.

"Wouldn't miss it for the world. My dancing shoes are getting a bit tight but whatever..." She looked deep into his eyes.

"Didn't I hear your father say that the traveller makes dancing shoes? Why! I'll get him to make you a pair." He promised.

"Pat! That's more than decent of you. You're so good to me." Reaching out she planted a kiss on his lips.

110

"I can make the shoes no bother but the Missie will need to come herself for the fitting. You do understand?" The traveller, a man about his own age informed Pat when he broached him on the subject. Mary duly went and had the measurements for the shoes taken.

"You know Missie that the right foot is always bigger than the left, not many people appreciate that?" He told her. Mary looked down at his tight curls and smiled.

"What's so funny, Missie?" He looked up into her eyes.

"Nothing, I was just admiring your curls."

"Thank you Missie, that's appreciated."

"Would you not keep calling me Missie? My name is Mary."

"Sorry Miss! I mean Mary but it's not my place to be so bold."

"It must be wonderful travelling the open spaces and meeting different people." Mary let out a sigh.

"It is that Mary, it is that... I'll tell you a few tales that I picked up during my travels. It will while away the time as I work on your shoes. Would you like to hear them?"

"Yes please." Mary sat down on seat next to him.

"It was when I stopped on the roadside outside Ballyhaunis..." The travelling man began his story as he continued working.

"Is that the time I must rush? There's a bit of 'Craic' in the rambling house this coming Saturday evening will my shoes be ready by then? I'll be back to hear more stories have no fear."

"You do that Mary and welcome. I'll have the shoes ready if I have to stay up half the night making them." He promised.

"Thank you. Why don't you come along to the Rambling house? What's your name?"

"It's John, but everyone that knows me calls me the travelling cobbler. I'll come along should I be welcome and thanks."

"Course you're welcome John, the rambling house is for all."

Saturday evening came and the rambling house soon filled up. The fiddler opened the evening with a rendering of reels and sets.

"Come on Pat, will you not dance the set with me?" Mary tried to lure Pat from his seat onto the flagged floor.

"You know that I'm no good at the sets. Wouldn't want to step on your new shoes, now would I? Why don't you ask the traveller to partner you?" He suggested.

"Good idea, you don't mind?"

111

"Why should I mind it's only a dance after all? He'll not be seeing you home, I hope." Pat laughed.

"Thank you John. You're a fine dancer I'll say that much for you. This is my fiancé Pat Slattery." She introduced them after the dance finished.

"Pleased to meet you Pat, now if you'll both excuse me."

"You're not going so soon, why the night is still young." Pat insisted.

"I've a lot to do before I take to the open road. Your fiancé is one fine dancer if I may say so. Took a lot of learning to dance like that."

"You must have spent half the night in Johns arms dancing." Pat reminded her on their way home.

"Pat Slattery, don't tell me that you were jealous of John? He told me so many stories of his travels. It must be wonderful to travel around the country like that." Mary let out a sigh as she looked nostalgically down at the caravan silhouetted in the moonlight. Pat noticed that Mary was a bit cool towards him of late and decided to approach her on the subject.

"Mary! Is something the matter, you don't seem to be yourself at all?"

"There's nothing the matter, what ever made you think that?"

"Sorry Mary! It's just that you're seldom about these days."

"That's the trouble, I'm always about. There's no place to go to." She grumbled.

"When we're married I'll take you wherever you want to go." Pat promised.

"When we're married is it? We'll have little time to spend travelling." Mary was in no mood to listen to Pat's promises.

"No need to bite my head off. What's eating you of late?"

"Nothing! Why should there be?" Rising she sauntered off alone.

The house was duly completed and with the nuptials finalised they moved in. Mary gave birth to a son in the spring of the following year. Pat took a delight in watching her singing to their son.

"I'll teach you to be a fine step dancer just like your father." She spoke to the child as she sat on the green sward looking into the valley.

"Like his father is it? God help him if he takes after me in the dancing." Pat came through the door.

"Oh! It's yourself Pat, I told you often enough not to creep up on me like that. It makes me nervous." Mary looked up startled.

112

"Sorry! I see John is back from his ramblings. Wonder how long he'll stay this time?" Pat informed her.

"Not too long I expect." Mary let out a sigh.

"We should go down to morrow and welcome him back. We could introduce him to our son? Why! You could get him to make you a new pair of dancing shoes? You're ever so fond of that old pair that he made more than a year ago, why I'll never know?" Pat suggested.

"You do that Pat, you do just that." Mary agreed.

"Call on him to morrow and invite him to tea. I'll be away at the cattle auction most of the day. I'll be home by nightfall all going well."

Pat returned to the house late the following evening and was surprised to find it in darkness.

"Mary! Where are you Mary?" Switching on the light he climbed the stairs. The bed and cot lay empty. Neither had been slept in. On his pillow lay an envelope. Picking it up he noted that it was in his wife's' handwriting and addressed to him. Tearing it open he read the contents...

Dear Pat,

Sorry! I thought you had best know about my son. I cannot live a lie. I have left and taken him back to his father, my travelling cobbler. I don't love you but I'll understand if you hate me. I wish you well. Please forgive me. Mary.

Pat rushed from the house and climbing the hillock looked down. The laneway was in darkness. He raced down the hill and came upon the last smouldering embers of the travelling cobblers fire. Looking he saw in the dying embers what remained of an old pair of dancing shoes.

Returning to the house he opened the wardrobe and searched for the box in which she kept her dancing shoes wrapped in tissue. The box was nowhere to be seen.

Too late he remembered the evening that he overheard Mary talking to her son...

'I'll teach you to be a fine step dancer like your father.'

'My Mary will soon have new dancing shoes, but not mine.' He sobbed as his tears filled his eyes.

THE SWEET SILVER BELLS

'Have you ever hear tell of the sweet Shannon bells
That once o'er the Shannon the Angelus did tell?
The story unfolds, or so I am told,
That it happened in Florence a long time ago.
A bell maker named Mathias, a vocation had he?
To honour our Lady, his Heavenly queen.

A gift he would make her that was gentle and sweet,
'Twas three silver bells her Angelus to greet'.
For ten weary years he sweated and toiled:
But his every last effort was useless and spoiled.
He prayed to the virgin for help in his task,
His prayers they were answered, on a night that was dark.

With tones that were gentle and sweet to the ear,
He fell to his knees our Lady to plead.
He listened in joy and sang in her praise:
As his three silver bells their sweet tones did raise.
"Now where will I hang them?" Mathias did pray:
For all to them listen and sing in her praise?

Looking out from his forge a grey friar he saw:
He was going to matins as he prayed' neath his shawl.
"Pray-tarry good friar, I have a request,
To honour Our Lady, my bells need a nest?
The bells you may have as a gift he declared.
Should you honour Our Lady thrice each day?"

Temptingly he rung them in the sweet morning breeze,
The three silver bells for the good friar to hear.
"The Angelus and Annunciation you daily will call:
At the morning and midday and then at the fall.
That's all the conditions that from you, I seek,
In honour of the virgin our Heavenly queen."

The good friar in spiritual gladness agreed,
To the request of Mathias so humble was he.
The bells they rang out o'er the fields and the forests:
From far and near they came, listened and wondered.
But not far from the shore plunderers were coming,
And the three silver bells they tore them asunder.

From the city of Florence all beauty was swept:
As Mathias looked up at the belfry he wept.
My sweet silver bells the blasphemers have stolen,
From crying and weeping his poor eyes were swollen.
The city of Florence was silent and still,
For no longer the Angelus called out at will.

I'll find them he promised his virgin and mother,
As Away from the shores of old Florence he wandered.
On England's green shore he sat and he pondered.
Where's my silver bells he cried and he wondered?
In a tavern he heard a group of monks talking,
In Latin, sweet bells he heard them exalting.

Mathias got flustered and rushed to their table:
"Please tell me good Sirs, is this but a fable?"
"It is not indeed for in Limerick we listened,
As the mighty great Shannon in the twilight it glistened.
The music was sweet and the tones so enchanting,
That the whole population they knelt and they chanted."

"Their beads they did number, ne'er a child did they slumber.
We tell you in truth for it makes us feel humble."
Mathias convinced, could no longer endure:
The praise of the bells, they were his that was sure.
"I plea for your blessing good friars, I beseech you,
Will you tell me you wise men, please tell me the news?"

" The bells are they safe, are they still in the steeple?
And in the safe care of good honest people?"
"A boat I will hire at the dawn of the morning,
To hear once again my sweet bells a calling."
The little boat entered the harbour at Limerick,
At the stern stood Mathias alone in his thinking.

115

His old eyes were sore and dimmed from their weeping;
Looking into the mist he was seeking a steeple.
Then lo and behold as the grey dawn was breaking;
O'er the mighty great river sweet music came creeping.
Mathias, he clung to the old wooden mast,
"They're my bells, my sweet bells, the ones that I cast."

He fell to his knees his poor heart near breaking,
As the sweet silver bells the Angelus awakened.
"O Virgin and mother, I've found them at last."
He slumped to the deck his life was now past,
"Oh sweet holy mother I'll not thee deny."
He prayed and cried o'er the Shannon rip tide,

The song of the bells continued to chime,
As poor old Mathias on the cold deck did die.
His life it was passing his mission was spent.
The heavens did open the sky it was rent,
As the three silver bells continued to chime.
The people of Limerick as one did arise.

'Neath the tower of Saint Mary's that cold winters day;
They carried his body to a well-selected grave.
In sight of his bells and the Angelus keeping,
His journey was o'er, free from cruel weeping.
From his grave he would bless them and pray for the people,
Who guarded his bells in their squat little steeple?'

Then it happened I tell you, I'll not it deny,
As the city was hidden in the grey morning mire,
Invaders they came up the Shannon that day,
To plunder the city and take the bells away?
The ghost of Mathias did moaned and did grumble,
And roused the great city from its sleep and slumber.

The people of Limerick to their cathedral ran,
And climbed to the steeple to the very last man.
They hacked at the ropes so firm and strong,
That held the three bells for so very long.
The bells they were taken to Curragower falls,
Those sweet silver bells no longer would call.

116

There's a lake in the Shannon near Ould Curragower,
Not known to that many outside Ould Limerick town.
When the tide it has ebbed and the waters have flown,
It rises I tell you serene and alone.
It's the lake of our Lady near the Castle of John,
It holds the sweet bells from the cathedral have gone.

Stand by the quayside, all silent and still,
And pause for awhile, say a prayer if you will?
For the soul of Mathias who shared with the people,
His sweet silver bells that once hung in their steeple
Do you doubt me my friend, or are you naïve?
Come out of your slumber come out from your sleep.
LOUIE BYRNE©

THE MYSTERY OF THE BELLS

The Mystery of the missing bells of Old Saint Mary's Cathedral has been local gossip for many, many years. How the bells of Florence came to Limerick has never been fully explained.

It is strongly believed that the bells were hidden in the Shannon during a raid on the city. It is also believed that before a disaster strikes the bells can be heard chiming. A gift from old Mathias no doubt?

Mathias lived in Florence with his wife and family where he owned a small foundry. He had an extraordinary devotion to 'Our Lady' and was determined to create a peal of bells that poured forth the sweetest and purest music.

After ten years of frustrated efforts he finally succeeded. He presented the bells to a community of local friars. He asked little in return except that the bells should be rung for the Angelus and Annunciation.

All went well until the city was sacked and the population mercilessly massacred. His wife and children were murdered and his silver bells stolen. Mathias, now a broken spirit wandered the world seeking his silver bells. Finally old and weary he came to the shores of England.

In a tavern where he went seeking alms he heard a group of travelling monks speaking of the wonderful bells that they had heard in Limerick, Ireland.

He sought passage in a ship sailing to Limerick. The ship sailed up the Shannon and at about six o'clock. As he stood on the deck holding on to the mast he heard them, his Sweet Silver bells. He fell to his knees and began to say the 'Angelus'.

As the music from the bells died into the night Mathias drew his last breathe. The people of Limerick bestowed the honour on him of burying him within the sound of his beloved bells in the grounds of Saint Mary's Cathedral. For two centuries the bells continued to chime out over the great river Shannon.

Then one misty morning plunderers came to raid the city. It is said that the ghost of the hermit Mathias, rose from his grave and warned the citizens of the imminent danger by ringing his sweet silver bells.

The people, man woman and child rushed to the cathedral, removed the silver bells and handed them over for safe keeping to one family. This family was bound by sacred oath never to disclose the whereabouts of the bells until the time was right.

It is strongly believed that the bells were hidden beneath the falls of 'Curragower' by a fisher folk from the Abbey River near by.

That family either died out or were drowned taking the secret of the bells with them. It is rumoured that at the right time a signal or sign will be given and the bells will rise like 'Arthur's Sword from 'Our Lady's Lake'.

THE AUCTION

DOES THE SUN SHINE ALONE FOR YOU?
Outside a grand mansion one dark stormy night,
A poor lad looked into a window so bright;
Watching the splendour, his heart filled with pain,
Thinking of his home where poverty reigned.
Suddenly he was pushed roughly aside,
And a voice said, "You're not wanted here."

He turned to the speaker, a lad like himself.
And he murmured these words in his ear.
"Does there sun shine alone for you?"
The rich lad turned in surprise.
"Your dad may be rich my lad,
For you're on the sunny side.

There be good mingled with rags.
In all the world over it's true
That a warm heart may beat
'Neath an old ragged vest,
Does the sun shine alone for you."

As your Seanachai I have told you many tales both sad and humorous. For telling this story I make no apology to Church or State. In my youth I saw too many poor souls carried on a cart dragged by old men from the poor house known as the City Home to the Yellow Hole in the haunted glen of Killeely, Limerick.

Although the City Home had its own chapel, Priests, nuns and convent not one to my knowledge ever attended a burial in the Yellow Hole. I wrote this little story to the memory of all those interred in the 'Paupers Field' Watchousecross known to us as... 'The Yellow Hole'...

The Lord of a grand mansion had died. His estate and its contents were to be broken up and sold at public auction by his immediate relatives.

119

On the day of the auction dignitaries from far and wide assembled to bid for the priceless treasurers. The auctioneer looked down from the rostrum and was pleased by the apparent wealth of the assembly. This would be a profitable auction he thought, on seeing the wealthy ladies and gentlemen take their places in the reserved chairs to the front of the rostrum.

At the back of the hall on an obscure bench sat an old man and woman alone. From their attire it would appear that what worldly goods they possessed they wore on their toil worn backs. The woman's hair was as white as the driven snow as was the man's. Both were bent with age and the old man's hands were enclosed in well-worn mittens. His hands were crippled with chilblains and arthritis. Every so often he would rub his hands together to ease the pain.

"That what comes from working long hours in the garden, come hail or sunshine." His wife sympathised.

"I know Mary, but it was my duty to look after the master's gardens." Once again he rubbed his hands vigorously together to ease the nagging pain.

"And a lot of thanks we got, you and me, Pat Slattery." Mary and Pat had worked all their lives within the confines of the estate. Both came from an orphanage in the city at an early age. Their parents had died from tuberculosis, the scourge of the period. They were sent to the great manor as girl and boy servants and were married in the estate chapel.

"The master promised us that we would have a home here as long as we lived." Pat pleaded with the relatives.

"We know nothing of any promises and anyhow we could not sell the estate with you occupying one of the tied cottages."

"But what is to become of us, we gave our lives to the estate?" Mary pleaded.

"There's always the workhouse, be out of your cottage by twelve noon come next Saturday." Came the curt order. That was all a bad memory now. The auctioneer's eyes focused on the two wretches sitting in the dark recess. Calling one of the porters he instructed him to go and question them as to their reason for being present at such a prestigious affair.

"Have we not the right to be here as much as they?" The old man rose wearily, yet proudly, to his feet and pointed to the grand assembly.

"Of course you have, I presume you will be bidding then?"

"We are here to buy the most valuable items in the hall, are we not my dear?" The old lady rose and taking her husband's enfeebled hands in hers smiled into his face.

"We are that Pat, so we are." The porter could not help but notice the warmth, love and affection that they had for each other. He returned to the rostrum and informed the auctioneer of their intentions.

"Will you look at that Pat, it was many the hour that I spent with the bees wax polishing the wood." A fine cabinet of rosewood and apple wood inlaid with brass and with heavy brass teardrop handles was brought into the auction room and placed temptingly before the anxious bidders.

"Whist Mary! We don't want to miss them now?" Pat gently chided her.

"Oh! Pray God Pat that nobody outbids us." She clung to her husbands arm as tears filled her old eyes.

"Don't fret Mary, you will have them just as I promised." With a reassuring smile he comforted her.

For seventy long years Mary and Pat had travelled life highways with scarcely a cross word between them. Pat would see to it that she got her wish, of that she was assured.

"Two thousand guineas I am bid for this fine piece, do I hear three?" The auctioneers voice echoed around the great hall.

"It won't be long now Mary, we must be patient." Old Pat affectionately hugged his wife.

"What if someone outbids us Pat, what then. Oh Pat! I could not bear it?" She cried.

"Mary! Grá geal mo cróide, (Love of my heart) I brought you here this bleak December day to buy you what your heart desires. You will have that wish granted have no fear." He dried her eyes and patting her hand he reassured her.

A break in the auction was called for at noon for refreshments in the grand dining room. The bidders left the hall and retired for their meal. Pat and Mary stayed behind sharing a can of tea and a few slices of dry bread. They would not be invited to the grand lunch.

"Who will bid me one thousand pounds?" Mary raised her head from Pat's lap and looked bewildered at the rostrum.

"Wake up Pat, Oh Pat! We may have missed them." Mary awoke with a start and looked anxiously towards the auctioneer.

"No Mary, there is little fear of that." He smiled and at the same time held her hands in his reassuringly.

"But Pat, perhaps as we slept...."

"Whist Allanah, you slept but I kept a vigil on the proceedings."

Towards evening the sale began to run down and many of the bidders had gone home. At the back of the hall sat the old couple waiting and watching. The cold ate into their old bones but they would not be deterred. Pat took off his well-worn coat and put it around the shoulders of his wife.

"Pat, what ails you at all, at all? Do you want to catch your death of cold?" Removing the coat she returned it to her husband with a gentle smile.

"We must be alert now Mary, they are bound to be in the next sale." Pat sat bolt upright on the bench. He wanted his presence to be noticed.

"Look Pat! It's them will you bid." She pulled at Pat's ragged sleeve.

"Will you hush Mary, don't appear so anxious." Pat was now fully alert and anxiously scanning every item that came to the rostrum.

"Who will give me sixpence for these?" The auctioneer laughed as he held them up in his hands.

"Who indeed, throw them in the rubbish and let's get on." Demanded a bidder. His sentiments echoed throughout the hall.

"I will bid a shilling, it is all we have in this world." Pat stood up his full height and proudly held up the coin for all to see. All eyes turned to the back of the hall where the old man and woman stood weeping.

"Sir, if you think so much of them then they are yours for nothing."

A hush fell on the assembly as the old man in bared feet and ragged clothes came proudly to the front of the rostrum. The auctioneer placed them gently into his outstretched palms.

"Tell me Sir! Why were you so anxious to bid your wordily possessions for such as these?" The auctioneer asked. The old man proudly stood on the rostrum and addressed the assembly.

"Ladies and gentlemen, begging your pardon it was on these that my Mary and me knelt on the day we were wed. To day is our Golden anniversary, is that not so, Mary. I would give my life if need be to present them to her? Thank you for listening to me." Taking his wife

in his arms he unashamedly hugged her to him. Arm in arm they left the hall carrying their prized possessions.

"You made me a proud woman back there, so you did Pat Slattery." The old woman smiled into his face.

"Where could I fly to without you my dove? Can a bird fly on one wing?" Pat felt the warmth of his wife's hand as she squeezed his gently.

That Christmas Eve a blizzard blanketed out the skyline as Pat and Mary sought in vain to find shelter. In the distance they heard the church bells calling the faithful to midnight service. Too exhausted to attempt the hazardous journey they lay down under the shelter of the nearest hedgerow.

"That was the best Christmas present I could ever wish for." Mary snuggled up to her Pat.

"For you my love, nothing is too much. Happy Christmas pet."

"And to you Pat, God bless and keep you." Then as an afterthought she added...

"I love you Pat and always will. You're a good man."

"You deserved better Mary, but no matter for what it's worth I'll always love and cherish you. We have each other and that is all that matters." Slowly closing their eyes they succumbed to sleep. As the church bells rang out the news of the infant birth, snowflakes slowly obliterated the resting place of Patrick and Mary Slattery.

They were found some days later locked in each other's arms. The old cushions that they valued so dearly they had placed behind their backs to offer some protection from the biting cold. They were buried, were Pat and Mary Slattery in an obscure corner side-by-side in a pauper's grave outside the village graveyard. The shilling was discovered in Pat's tattered pocket, not enough to buy the poorest coffin or to buy them a burial plot. The shilling however bought a bail of straw to cover them and to pay the gravedigger.

Leaning on his slán, the gravedigger looked into the lonely yellow hole. Placing the slán against the hedge he picked up the two cushions. Climbing into their grave he gently placed a cushion under the grey locks of Mary. Lifting the head of Pat he dusted away the snow from his face and placed the other cushion under his head.

"God be merciful to you whoever you are. Is there nobody at all left to say a hungry prayer over you?" His voice echoed around the empty

123

paupers graveyard as he gently covered their faces with the straw. Kneeling he said the 'Poor man's mass' over them before filling in the grave.

There would be no sexton to ring the bell and no cleric to pray over them. No tears would be shed o'er their grave. You see old Pat and Mary Slattery were, like so many others the flotsam of this world.

On the other side of the wall in the graveyard workmen were busy erecting a huge obelisk of dressed granite stone over the tomb of Lord Russell Gray late master of Patrick and Mary Slattery, his humble servants. The granite stone may tell the story of his lordship for a time before it deteriorates and falls.

The story of Pat and Mary Slattery will live on so long as there are writers to tell the tale.

To day a neat little brook flows past the overgrown grave of Patrick and Mary Slattery. Over it grows a small copse. In its solitude a family of robins built their nest many years ago and their generations are still there to this day.

Where is it? Now that would be telling!

The Yellow Hole

That ould wooden cross stands ten feet tall,
Its obscene shadow like a vulture's call.
Where they buried the paupers in yellow holes,
Ne'er cast a prayer! Forgot their souls.
No granite stone to mark the spot,
No obelisk tall to forget them not.
On the day of judgement when the roll is called,
They'll stand, these paupers ten feet tall.
Christ looked down and called each one,
Leave your mortal body from earth be gone.
Come home to me, your suffering's o'er,
My door is open you're welcome home.
These were the words the Lord he spoke,
As o'er old Clare the dawn it broke.
Then angels came to comfort them,
Their troubles now were at an end.

Louie Byrne©

124

THE CHURCH OF THE STATUES

'Neath the walls of old Limerick now silent and still,
Stands the church of Saint Michael, beside an old mill.
The high altar's gone and the statues are few,
In the Church of the Statues that I once knew.

'Twas in that old church that my family prayed,
And from its grand portals on Mass days we strayed.
My granddads and grandmas to mention but a few,
In the Church of the Statues they prayed in the pews'.

My father, God rest him one cold Christmas day,
Was placed near the manger where the Infant child lay.
In the graveyard outside stood our graves and our tombs,
'Neath the Church of the Statues not far from my school.

The church is not trendy the clerics did say,
Those altars and statues they just cannot stay.
And so the mementos that our generations gave,
From the Church of the Statues were banished away.

Saint Michael still raises his sword with his might,
As that demon old Lucifer he soon puts to flight.
The fonts are now empty and covered in dew,
Outside of the Church of the Statues that I once knew.

The baptismal font in which I as a child,
The good priest did dip me my conversion in mind.
'Good friends where's it gone?' I asked of the few,
From the Church of the Statues that I once knew.

'Twas mothers last wish to be taken back there,
For her requiem mass where her late husband once lay.
We granted her wish I'm proud to relate,
In the Church of the Statues one cold winters day.

125

The ghosts of the graveyard they moan for they're lost,
Their last resting place for a car park has gone.
The holy well too, where the fairy tree bloomed,
Has gone from the Church of the Statues that I once knew.

The church is now empty where my folk did meet,
From Arthur's Quay to Francis Street;
And Anne, who sold apples outside Quinn's door,
In the Church of the Statues will pray no more.

I too am growing old I dare to say!
As to the old church sometimes, often I stray?
And there in the shadows the mementos I see,
In the Church of the Statues where once we did meet.

From the Church of Saint Michael my leave I took,
With a tear in my eye and no backward look.
As out from the belfry a white dove he flew,
From the Church of the Statues that I once knew.

This little poem may need a little explaining and I crave the
indulgence of the reader. Saint Michaels Church in Denmark Street
Limerick was known for its beautiful Italian statues and altars. These
were purchased from funds raised by people of the 'Parish' and
donated to the church. The statues and altars were so numerous and
beautiful that it gained the name 'The Church of the Statues.' Times
changed and the parish moved out from the city centre leaving the
'Church of the Statues' without its congregation. The graveyard was
sold off for a car park and the baptismal font and statues banished
from the church. Today the old church stands alone apart from the
odd mass and the few old folk that visit it to say a prayer and perhaps
hoping to meet an old face or to reminisce on times long past. Who
knows who cares?

THE FAMINE CAVES

Don't question me why I was in Malin that night,
On my way to the Gaeltach I thought I would drive,
To view the last sight from old Donegal,
Where so many Gaels to America were called.

I stood on the cliff top in nostalgic dreams,
I dreamed of the famine and the sorrows once seen.
The waves lapped the rocks and the ocean did sing,
'Twas the voice of the Dolphins singing a dirge.

They sang of the people that died in the caves,
From eating the mollusc's, the caves now their grave.
Who were they I thought, those sons of the Gaels?
Their voices now silent, in agony once raged?

Far out in the ocean a light I did see,
It traversed I tell you o'er the blue sea.
I looked and I wondered what a sight to behold,
This light from the Heavens, its message unfold.

Closer and closer that light did approach,
I stood apprehensive, I stood all alone.
The light it did enter a cave to my right,
O'er parched bones it rested then vanished from sight.

My thoughts they did wander to a time long ago,
When a star from the east a new life did show.
I thought of the infant, who was born in a cave,
Then I knew of its meaning, I knew why it came.

LOUIE BYRNE©

127

LAST THROW OF THE DICE

THE OPTIMIST

'Am I the one in the maddening crowd
That a rainbow seeks on a distant cloud?
There's hardly a breath in the morning air,
Yet the leaves are tossed here and there.'
Here is a story that will bring a tear to many the eye. Where it took
place matters not...

Chapter One

Pat Slattery sat on the seat in his potting shed, an obligatory cigarette stuck in the corner of his mouth. A long length of burnt ash hung precariously along its length. Pat was engrossed in finishing off the young seedlings. A stabbing pain in his chest caused him to stop working...

"A touch of indigestion after the cucumber sandwiches." He murmured as he tapped his chest to relieve the pain. When the pain eased he returned to continue potting up the seedlings. With the task completed he began to tidy up the workbench. Whatever else one might say of him, Pat was one meticulous worker when it came to keeping the workplace tidy. As he cleaned a trowel he again felt a stabbing pain in his chest. Once again he put it down to indigestion and placing the trowel on a hanger he locked the shed door and returned to the house.

"I've potted up the last of the seedling geraniums, Mary. They look good and strong should make a nice show in the summer." He called to his wife Mary busy in the kitchen.

"That's good news, now would you like a nice cup of tea, you've earned it?"

"That would be much appreciated, would you ever bring it into my study?" Pat crossed the floor and entered a small room off the sitting room. In a corner resting on a small desk sat a home computer and a printer. In a blue office tidy were several pens, pencils etc:

Pat sat down and switched on the computer. He had decided to write a book and had spent the past twelve months putting his idea into print. As he began working on his manuscript his wife entered the study and placed a cup of tea discreetly to one side. She knew from past experience that she should not place the cup too near to where he was working.

"Thanks Mary, the book is coming along fine. Will you read some of it to night and tell me what you think. I wonder will my work be appreciated?"

"Of course it will and from what you've written so far it is a good story. Now all you need is a publisher." She encouraged him.

Pat suddenly stopped writing and held his hand to his chest.

"Is there something the matter Pat?" His wife looked worried as she watched him fight for breath.

"It's nothing to worry about love, just a touch of indigestion, I fear." Dismissing her concern he again tapped his chest.

"Perhaps you should leave the writing for now. You've done enough for to day. What with all the work in the potting shed and now this?"

"You're right as usual Mary, I might sit down and study the new seed catalogues." Turning off the computer he returned slowly to his favourite chair in the sitting room.

"You forgot your tea." His wife placed the cup on the small table beside the chair. As he sat in the chair he began to feel uncomfortable.

"Mary! I think I'll lie down and rest, I don't feel all that great." Without waiting for her reply he rose slowly and retired to his bed.

It was morning when his wife holding a cup of tea in her hand awakened him.

"What time is it Mary. I must have slept late?"

"You had a restless night, perhaps you should go and see Doctor Flynn for a check up?" She suggested.

"I feel fine thanks, that rest has done me a world of good." Finishing his tea he dressed and returned to the sitting room.

"I'll do a little more work on my manuscript this morning. I feel inspiration coming on." He half laughed.

"You do that and take it easy. I have a lot of shopping to do, anything you want?"

"Nothing at all love, take care now."

She returned sometime later to find her husband busy printing out the manuscript.

"So you have finished it then? Good for you."

"Not yet, I'm running off a few chapters to send to publishers."

129

Mary prepared the meal before calling him from the study.

"How is that for timing, Mary? Just finished as you called me."

That night his chest pains returned. As the night wore on his pains increased in severity. His wife decided that there was something seriously wrong with him and phoned for the doctor. Doctor Flynn came to the house in the early hours of the morning and examined Pat.

"Can I use your telephone, please Mary?" Removing his stethoscope he asked.

"Certainly doctor, but what is the matter with Pat?"

"That is what we are about to find out. I am sending him to the hospital for a full medical check up." He studied the concern showing on her face.

Pat spent the next week in hospital undergoing several tests. Finally he was returned home and told that he must take it easy. He had suffered several mild heart attacks. However should he take care of himself and give up smoking then all should be well.

He continued pottering round his greenhouse but was finding it tiring. Finally he had to admit that this was too much and confined himself to the house. He devoted more time to his manuscript now that he was unable to work in the garden. Occasionally when he became brain dead he would potter into the garden and do a little work.

He continued sending chapters of his work to publishers but without success. Yes, they agreed it was a good story line but as an unknown author he stood little chance. Each in turn wished him luck.

Spring gave way to summer and as yet he had not found a publisher. Perhaps when the book was completed they would appreciate it more he thought. As his health continued to deteriorate it was suggested that they should sell the house and purchase a small bungalow.

It would be less of a burden to Mary and a comfort to Pat, as he would no longer have to climb the stairs.

So the sign went up 'House for sale.' Pat watched nostalgically as the sign swayed in a gentle breeze. Who would the new owners be and would they appreciate all the work that he had put into the garden?

There was little time left to dwell on the subject for within a week the house was sold. Pat did not meet the new owner of his house and beloved garden. One afternoon after Mary had taken herself off to the shops he decided that he must return and take a last look at his old home.

Picking up the telephone he dialled for a taxi. The taxi stopped outside the house and Pat alighted.

He peeped over the neat hedge and on into the garden. He was surprised and delighted to see that it was as neat and tidy as he had left it. 'If only I could get a glimpse of my back garden', he thought.

"I see you admiring my garden, everyone seems to stop and look." Pat was startled when a man carrying a hoe appeared from behind a hedge.

"I cannot take any credit for the garden, it is the work of the previous owner. There are different flowers in the beds whenever I look. You should see the back garden and his greenhouse; it's a picture to behold? I do my best to keep it all trim and tidy. Would you like to see his back garden?"

"Yes please" Pat leaning heavily on his walking stick followed the owner. Up the familiar path, through the wicker gate and on into the rear garden they went.

His Koi Carp were still in the pond and as he approached the pond they came to the surface to greet him.

"They seem to know you, were you owner of this house?"

"I must own up this was my paradise." Pat waved his cane over the garden. He went on to tell why he had to sell.

"I'm sorry to hear of your illness and if ever you want to come and see the garden feel no obligation. You could be an inspiration to an amateur like myself."

Nothing it would seem had changed it was as if he never left it. Time it would seem had stood still in the garden. He returned home content within himself that his beloved garden was in capable hands.

Chapter Two

One afternoon he collapsed from a massive stroke and was rushed to hospital. He was now paralysed down his left side. After several weeks in intensive care he was returned home in a wheelchair unable to walk and barely able to talk.

Mary would now have to attend to all his needs, He stubbornly insisted that he was getting better and would soon be up and about but she knew that time was not on his side. With so much time on his hands he began to brood over his book.

"Mary, Do you think that I'll ever find a publisher to accept my work?"

"Of course. Now stop worrying there's plenty of time and lots more publishers to be contacted." She consoled him.

Next morning he heard the letterbox flat spring open.

"Mary will you please get the post, it might be good news?" He called from his sick bed. She went into the hall and collected what mail there was. One letter was from the latest contact.

She tore the envelope open and read the contents. It thanked him for sending his manuscript but regretfully...' She threw the letter into the fire and returned to his bedside.

"Nothing in the post, but that's a good sign, they must be considering it for publication." She lied.

In the afternoon as her husband slept she sat down to read the paper. It was then that her eyes focused on a small advertisement. She read it over and over again unable to believe her eyes. Wanted by American publishing house manuscripts for publication in the U.K/U.S.A. Please telephone...'

Mary read the advertisement again unable to comprehend what she was reading. Picking up the telephone she dialled the number, A girl with an American accent answered.

"Hi! My name is Josephine, how may I help you?" She drooled.

Mary related how her husband desired to have his book published and of his illness.

"Sorry to her of your husbands illness, Maam! Please send us the manuscript at once and we will let you know if it has any potential within a week, have a nice day." Drawled the voice at the other end.

The phone clicked all was silent. Mary replaced the receiver unable to believe her luck.

Here at last was a publisher willing to consider her husbands work. Next morning she carefully wrapped her husband's manuscript and took it to the post office. With a kiss for luck she handed it over the counter. The manuscript was now on its way to the publishers in London. She was taken aback when two day later a letter arrived from the publishers. That was quick reading, she thought. Then she read their letter...

Dear Pat.

We have read your manuscript and are pleased to tell you that not alone myself but the whole staff here in our London office were more than impressed with your work. We were so overcome by the story line that we took the liberty of sending it to our World Wide headquarters in the United States of America for their assessment.

We hope that you will not be offended by us taking this liberty. Your work is so outstanding that we felt our parent company would not wish to lose this opportunity to access the contents. You should receive a reply directly from them within a week or so.

Sincerely Yours
Josephine.

P.S The enclosed get well card is from all the staff here. God bless you.

She went to the bedroom and read the letter to her husband and then presented it to him.

"How kind of them to show so much concern. I wonder if they will publish it?" Laying the letter to one side he looked towards the window.

"They more or less say that they will publish it. Look at their address, it is from their World Wide address in London, no less?" She returned the letter to her husband for verification.

She continued administrating to her husbands needs and at the same time keeping an anxious eye on the post. Weeks passed without a reply. Perhaps they had read the manuscript and rejected it, she thought.

"Don't get so upset, Mary. It's a long way to America. They will need some time to assess its merit as they say." Taking a fit of coughing he lay back on the pillows exhausted.

Three weeks passed without any reply from the United States

"That's that Mary, we may as well say good bye to them. Still not to worry there are many more outlets to contact." She could tell by the tone of his voice that he was disappointed.

Two days later a rather large envelope dropped through their letterbox. Mary picked up the envelope and noted the postmark. 'Pittsburgh Penn'. The letters danced before her tear filled eyes. They had not forgotten them. Slicing open the envelope she discharged a large selection of literature.

This she brushed to one side as she searched for their accompanying letter. In her agitated state she must have missed it for it was sitting on top of the pile. Reading the contents she was proud by the commendations bestowed on her Pat. This would definitely be a tonic to him. The letter read...

Dear Pat,

We have read the manuscript and have no hesitation in endorsing the findings of our London office. This is indeed a masterpiece and a work of note. Your unique way with words offer a philosophical exploration of a topic that is as complex as time itself. You have an envied talent that is both evocative and to the point. This is a masterpiece that rightly deserves a place with the most distinguished writers.

It tells the world that **Pat Slattery** is an author to be read. However you must appreciate that as an unknown author you will find it nigh impossible to find a publisher willing to gamble his money on your book, dynamic though it is.

Many brilliant authors found it impossible to find a publisher willing to accept their works. There was Charles Dickens, T.S. Elliott, George Bernard Shaw and the Bronte sisters just to mention a few. They did as you know find fame and fortune and how? By self-publication through a subsidiary company.

134

This is where we can assist you for we are a subsidiary company with offices in the U.K and the U.S.A. We have been in continuous business since 1800. Our reputation is second to none and we have distribution agents through both countries and worldwide.
Your book will be circulated among editors of all national papers for their review and we are confident that they will endorse our findings. Copies will be sent to all universities in Britain, Ireland and the United States.'
She could hardly believe her luck at finding such a publisher. She was not sure however but that they were exaggerating her husbands' talent. Still if they were convinced that her husband was a genius then who was she to question them? She was about to take their letter into the bedroom for her Pat to read when she stopped and read the small print at the bottom of the letter...
Leading critics read our books and have no hesitation in recommending them to the their readers. The copyright of the book would be registered in his name and would remain so for the next fifty years. He would retain all commercial rights to the book.
What a very generous company they were she again thought...
Hearing her husband calling she put the letter to one side and went to attend to his needs. He was far from well and was having difficulty with his breathing. Seeing his distressed state she immediately called the doctor.
The doctor having taken one look at Pat immediately sent for a supply of oxygen to relieve his distress. Pat was rushed to hospital in a critical state later that night.
She ignored the letters coming on a daily basis from the publishing company as she devoted all her energy to attending to her sick husband. They wanted the book in the bookshops before Christmas. She should not miss this golden opportunity. Should she fail to meet the deadline then they regretted that publication would have to be put back for twelve months.
That evening she went to the hospital to learn that there was a further deterioration in his condition.
"Mary! The manuscript is for you when I'm gone, it will bring in a little support to you." He held her hand in his.

Chapter Three

That evening she glanced through the literature and their letters. Putting these to one side she dictated a letter to them giving them permission to publish the book as soon as possible.

"There! I'll say nothing to Pat until we receive the first copy." She placed it inside and envelope and sealed it. Picking up one of the glossy pages of information in order to copy the address she noticed that she had not read it. It was then that the bombshell burst. They would require a contribution towards the cost of publication. This she could pay by instalments. They would pay her 45% of the retail price of the book more than any other publisher. In addition she would receive four dozen copies free to give to her friends. Reading on she came to the sum requested to defray part of the cost for publishing and distribution. The sum requested was a staggering $7.000.U.S.

She tore up her letter and dictated a further letter explaining that her husband was seriously ill and that she was reluctant to part with any money at present. The book would have to wait until he recovered.

Again she received a prompt reply pointing out the great opportunity she was missing. Great writers had their work overlooked because they hesitated.

The pressure was now on, she loved her husband dearly and knew how much he looked forward to seeing his book in print. Still she hesitated. Shortly afterwards he was sent home there was nothing more that they could do for him. He was now in the hands of providence.

"Mary! Did the American publishers that were so nice ever reply?" He would ask over and over again.

"Not as yet but you know these things take a long time, be patient." Finally in desperation she went to the bank and withdrew the deposit money and together with the contract sent it to the publishers London office.

She received an acknowledgement by return and at the same time a reminder that the book would not be published until all payments were met in full. It was Pats wish to see the book in print and the savings belonged to them both. When the first two thousand were sold it would see a tidy profit to them. Further more after that the publishers would print all further copies and publish them at their own expense. There was no need for her to worry; yet somehow she was apprehensive. It was all too good to be true. She sent off the final instalment and waited in anticipation for the first copies to arrive.

One day a post office van arrived at her door and deposited two large sacks of American mail on her doorstep. Each sack contained two dozen books wrapped carefully in bubble wrap to protect them. She took a bundle from one sack and opened the protective covering. She studied the book and ran her hand over the dust cover...

'Last Throw of the Dice' By Pat Slattery

Tears filled her eyes as she read and reread the title in gold lettering. Finally she turned to the back cover and there was a photograph of her Pat smiling up at her. It was worth it after all, she thought. This was a fitting tribute to a great author.

Slowly she approached the bedroom and hesitated outside the door. Wiping the tears from her eyes she opened the door and entered the bedroom. Her husband lay on his side in the bed breathing deeply through his oxygen mask.

"Are you awake Pat?" She spoke quietly. There was no response.

She retreated from the room and gently closed the door. In the kitchen she made herself a cup of tea and sat down to read the book. It was indeed a lovely story written from the heart. The striking of the clock awakened her.

"Goodness me I must have dozed off." She spoke aloud. Again she went to the bedroom and opening it she called to her husband.

" Are you awake Pat? Do you fancy a cup of tea?"

"I'm awake and thanks, would you ever switch on the light?" Slowly she turned the dimmer switch as the room was filled with light.

"How are you feeling love? I have a little surprise for you." She removed the pillows from under his head and fluffed them up.

"What's the surprise Mary? Not visitors, I'm not fit enough to see anyone."

"Something far better than that, just you wait." Returning to the kitchen she prepared a tray for her husband. In the centre of the tray she placed a copy of his book. Opening the door she approached his bed and placing the tray to one side she helped him to sit up. Placing the tray before him on the bed she stood back allowing him to appreciate his work.

137

"They done it Mary, they published my book. Doesn't it look grand and with my picture on the back?" This was the first time in months that he had smiled. She felt that it was now worth all the sacrifice. She felt a proud woman, did Mary as she looked down at her dying husband. Tears of joy and sorrow overtook her, yet she remained steadfast.

"What do you think now, Pat Slattery? You are a famous author."

"I was hoping this would happen Mary. It was not out of vanity but to leave you a little security when I'm..." Tears filled his eyes as he tried to speak.

"Eat you supper love before it gets cold. You can read the book at your leisure later." She dismissed his concern.

She left the room pleased with her effort. She had brought a little comfort to her dying husband. All the midnight oil that he burnt writing it was his way of repaying her for all her years of devotion. She sent a copy of his book to the local newspaper and they generously published an article about Pat and his book. Daily she scoured the bookshops searching for her husband's book. Whatever was the matter she wondered; why was his book not in the bookshops? Pat kept asking how the sale of his book was doing. What could she tell him? She wrote to the publishers enquiring as to why there were no books in the shops. Their reply made it clear that there was no distributor. She could buy the book from them at a discount of 65% but she would have to pay the freight cost. She knew that she would never see a penny from their investment. The bookshops would require a 50% reduction on the retail price should they accept the books for sale. She went to the local bookstore and approached the manager. She asked if any representative of the publishers had approached him with a copy of the book.

"Tell me Mam, what's the name of the publishers and who are their distributors?"

"The publishers are 'Global Publishers' and they are based in London and America. She went on to tell him of the glowing reports she received from the company about her husbands' book.

"I have a copy of his book here if you would like to see it?" She produced a copy from her basket.

"Mrs Slattery, please! I hate to tell you this but the papers are littered with such advertisements. These people are Vanity publishers and will

138

publish anything-even scribbles from a lavatory wall. They prey like parasites on the old and young alike so long as you can pay them. For what they charge you could have five times as many copies printed privately. If I had my way I'd ban all of them. They are parasites. Now I'm not saying that your husband's book is not a winner. The only way you will get your book into a bookshop is by you becoming a foot soldier. It is deception on a large scale as you found out to your cost too late, I fear. The letter you received is a stock letter and you were deceived. I am so sorry."

"Oh my God! What have I done? I sent them all of our savings. They knew my circumstances yet they took all our savings, how cruel. Whatever will Pat say when he finds out? This news will surely be the death of him."

"May I suggest seeing that he is so very ill that you tell him nothing of this. These people feed on the gullible and unwary as I told you. They are sharks and that is an insult to sharks. I find it hard to believe how these people can live with themselves? I'm sorry I cannot be more helpful?"

"Thank you for you time." Mary left the shop and walked down the street.

"Wait Mrs Slattery." A hand was laid gently on her shoulder.

"What is it now? More bad news I suppose?" Taking her handkerchief from her pocket she wiped her eyes.

"No! This is yours I believe." The bookstore manager held out the copy of Pats book.

"Ah yes! Pats book?" She wiped a tear from the cover.

"Tell me, how many copies do you have?" He asked.

"About four dozen, Why?"

"Would you ever let me have them and I'll put them on a shelf in the store? I'm well acquainted with the editor of a national newspaper and I'll get him to take a photograph of you standing next to Pat's book. You never know you may yet strike lucky. You could show the picture to your husband." He smiled assuring her that all was not yet lost.

"That is more than kind of you, Pat would appreciate it. Thank you! Thank you." She returned home and assured her husband that his book was holding pride of place in the largest bookshop in town.

That evening having seen to her husbands needs she sat down and composed a long letter to the publishers 'Global Publishers'. She told them what the manager had said and hoped that he was mistaken. Knowing that her husband was dying she felt that they would not exploit the situation. She reminded them of their obligation to publish and distribute the book. Their reply only confirmed what the manager had told her. The so-called company was like a Jekyll and Hyde.

Should anyone wish to purchase her husbands book they could purchase a copy from them. They had no distribution bases in America or the U.K. They rented a small office space in London and one in Pittsburgh. This was the sum total asset of 'Global Publishers' Worldwide. It was a complete Scan. One evening as she sat beside the bed of her dying husband the telephone rang.

"Hallo! Mrs Slattery speaking." She whispered.

"This is the manager of the bookstore, Mrs Slattery. I'm glad that I found you home. How is Pat?"

"Not well. Not well at all, thanks for your concern." She was about to return the handset.

"Wait! I really am sorry to hear that but don't hang up. I have great news for you. The books are sold and I have a cheque for you."

"I don't get out much what with Pat being so poorly. However that is good news, he will be so pleased. Thank you! You've been so kind."

"Pleased he should be there's a growing demand for the book. I'm asking your permission to send the last copy to a publisher friend of mine"

"By all means do that, you have been more than a friend to us, thanks."

"Sorry but you don't seem to understand, I want you to know what a good investment it is."

"Investment! What will the American publishers say?"

"Let them say what they like. This is Pats book and you paid for it?"

"Very well you go ahead and do what you think best." Mary traumatised from all the worry agreed.

Slowly she replaced the telephone as her husbands hand slipped from hers. The manager heard the telephone click as the call was terminated.

Taking the final copy from the window the manager carefully wrapped it and sent it to the publisher.

Mary watched as her husband's health took a dramatic turn for the worst. No longer able to speak he lay in his bed looking forlorn out of his bedroom window.

Daily she would bring fresh flowers and place them on the window sill.

One morning she received a telephone call from the bookshop manager.

"Great news Mrs Slattery, your husbands book is number one, the best seller.

"Thank ...'

She heard a thud coming from her husband's bedroom and dropping the receiver she rushed into the room. Her husband's book that held a place of pride next to the fresh flowers was lying on the floor.

"Sorry love, the wind must have caught it," She looked down at her husband and she knew that the dice had been thrown for the last time...

Mary stopped outside the window of a large bookstore in London some weeks later. Holding centre stage in the large display of the best selling book was a photograph of her husband.

'**Last Throw of the Dice'** By Pat Slattery

'Pat would be proud were he here' She spoke aloud. Wiping a nostalgic tear from her eye she entered the flower shop next door...

Taking a tissue from her handbag she wiped the headstone.

'That's better Pat, don't you think?" She read the inscription on the base of the stone...

'**Last Throw of the Dice.'**

She placed the flowers neatly beside the inscription just as Pat would have liked.

MY DOG BRUNO

We met old friend when both were young,
In fallowed fields outside that wood.
"Do you want a pup?" The stranger asked.
You looked at me and began to bark.
With mottled coat and tail so long,
Who'd have you even for a song?

I looked you up and down old friend,
You wagged your tail and cocked your head.
You were so thin, so small and weak,
I'm sorry I said, he's not what I seek.
You cast your eyes upon the ground,
Your hopes I dashed your fate was bound.

Then waters deep your life would seize,
Who'd take a pup riddled with fleas?
The stranger pulled the noose up tight,
I knew your fate once you left my sight.
Reaching down I stroked your head
You licked my hand no words were said.

In your brown eyes I read your grief,
Give me this chance, give me relief:
How could I let you die this way?
In river deep, a watery grave.
Reaching out I took the rope
Somehow my friend with life we'd cope.

Through hungry years and harvest fields,
We worked and played, just you and me.
In fun and frolic, in times of care,
When birds migrated and trees were bare.
What care had we, just you and me?
Two orphan ruffians and life's sweet dreams.

142

Your gait one day I saw was slow,
Your whiskers too were turning gold.
I knew old friend that Father times,
Would call for you, no longer mine.
But I would cherish the love you gave,
To an orphan child that soft spring day.

I'll not forget you old pal of mine,
Nor the times we spent just you and I,
In woods and fields and tree filled glens,
With rabbits, voles and secret dens.
And there to lie in fields of velvet sheen,
And dream our dreams of what might be.

You'll never more in fields of green,
Chase rabbits, hares and rats with glee.
You've gone old friend to pastures new,
To chase the elk with Finn McCoul.
No more the orchard gate you'll watch,
Lest I your master should get caught.

LOUIE BYRNE©

143

FINAL FAREWELL

I sit alone, I feel life's' tears,
My dog he rests beneath my feet:
There's no place left for me to roam,
I've seen it all, wild oats I've sown.

In humble cottage I rest my head,
A bundle of straw my only bed.
I've stories to tell of places I've been,
Of sights and wonders I have seen.

Alas! Who now to listen, whom to tell,
Of what has been, of the life I led?
Winter winds howl round my door,
My life now spent, I'm going home.

Wearily I rise to open the door,
My dog set free, the fields to roam.
Where are they that made good cheer,
And drank a round or two with me?

The night's cold wind is closing in,
Please God forgive me all my sins.
So now farewell to you good friends,
My life, my dreams are at an end.

LOUIE BYRNE©

Saint Columcille's encounter with Pat Slattery

REALITY

'And here at home by Shannon side,
I watch the river, the rising tide.
Yet as I sit and as I dream,
The waters turn, it's now a stream.'

Reality. Louie Byrne

Ballyjamesduff, is a neat little town that's situated half way between Cavan and Heaven. It was when sitting by the shores of Nadreegeel Lough that I discovered the following Sean Scéal in that old grey head of mine...

It was a fine summers evening and the whole world seemed to be at peace. The birds sang in the trees and the fish jumped in the crystal clear stream. Saint Columcille strolled along the bank of the river towards Coothill with not a care in the world. Round a bend in the bank he saw a minstrel sitting dejectedly on a hard carraig. (Rock)

"Bennact an seaséir leat." (Blessings of the season on you) Greeted the saint. There was no response from the minstrel. He sat with a look on his face that would turn buttermilk sour. His mute Feadán (flute) sticking out from the top pocket of his coatamore told the story.

"What ails you, my fine fellow?" The saint inquired as he came and sat beside him on the carraig. There was no response and to make matters even worse he turned his back on the good saint. What an insult you may rightly ask to the holy man. Yet the saint was not disconcerted in the least.

"Will you at least play an old tune on your feadán for me?" Again the saint tried to make conversation.

"What is your name if I may be so bold to ask?" He continued.

"Your reverence, my name is Pat Slattery and with no disrespect to the cloth you will have to excuse my bad manners. Under the circumstances I cannot play for you."

"What circumstances, surely it cannot be all that bad that it stops a Cavan minstrel from playing a tune?"

"Not alone is it bad but it is far worse. Far worse, your reverence. You see I buried my Mary yesterday. I am now all-alone in the world with not a soul to warm my back. Tá mo cróide brónac" (My heart is broken). Hanging his head he looked across at the bleak hillside.

145

"You must have loved her dearly? I am indeed sorry for your troubles." The saint offered his condolences.

"Thanks your grace. Love her? She meant everything to me. Kind words never healed a broken heart, nor for that matter warmed a sorrowful widowers' back. 'Ochone! Ochone! My Fedán will never again touch my lips to my dying day. Ochone! Ochone! Ochone! Ta mo croide brisead" (Sorrow, my heart is broken). *Pat let out such a moan that it struck a cord with the gentle saint.*

"My friend never have I witnessed such love and devotion. You shall be united with your Mary." The saint rose to his feet and holding his crosier towards the heavens he began to chant in Latin.

The minstrel looked shocked as a bolt of lightening struck the hook of the crosier. He was so shocked that he nearly had a heart attack and was about to join his Mary in her grave. He nearly had another as the smoke from the bolt subsided. Out from it stepped none other than his wife Mary.

"Oh Mary! Mary allanah you are back to me." Jumping off the carraig he ran to embrace his wife.

"Don't give me any of your Mary allanah, you, you scannróir." (Miser) she stuttered.

"What ever ails you Mary, Gra geal mo cróide." (Joy of my heart)

"Ails me! I'll tell you what ails me. You could not see your way to give me a decent torrám agus socraid (wake and funeral), You old scannróir." She placed her hands on her hips and belated him as if she had never died.

"But Mary love, did I not play all the tunes that you loved so much at your wake? Give me credit for that."

"Play them you may have but not for my benefit. Did you not ask Louie Byrne to take the hat around? Can you deny it?"

"I did, I did that I must confess but only to pay the offerings to the good sagart (priest) himself."

"And when may I ask did you intend to pay the Priest and you half way to Cavan before my bones were laid in the sod?"

"Now Mary they are hard words, hard words indeed." Pat felt hurt and looked to the saint for guidance. Now the good saint on seeing all the bitterness between them was having second thoughts. He tried to placate the situation but only made matters worse.

146

"I'm glad that you brought me back your reverence, all respect to your holy office. It gives me the opportunity to show you what a specimen I married." Mary continued her rhetoric without respite. She continued for some considerable time to castigate poor Pat.

Saint Columcille tiring of the whole charade decided that Mary and Pat had more than enough of each other in life. Their nuptials were not the bed of roses that Pat would have him believe. Rising wearily to his feet with Mary still giving him earache he looked towards the heavens. Again raising his crosier he prayed aloud and once again the crook was struck by lightening. When the smoke and flame died away Pat stood alone in the middle of the road. Of Mary there was neither sight nor sound.

"Will you oblige me by playing 'The rake in the rafters?" Requested Saint Columcille as if nothing had happened.

"To be sure your reverence, for is it not a charitable favour you done for my Mary."

"Why do you say that Pat?"

"Well sure as I'm standing here was it not yourself that finally managed to shut her up?"

The music from the Feadán of Pat could be heard as far away as Ceannus Mór as they wended their way to the village of Finnea by Lough Sheelin shore.

SINGING IN THE WIND

Come with me past Shannon side,
Then follow me past Sarsfield's ride.
Pause and listen to the trees that sing,
Is it Bean-Ó-Sidhe crying in the wind?

Listen! Hush! Can you not hear?
The horses neigh, the clash of steel?
In Caherconlish no church bells ring,
As the Bean-Ó-Sidhe sings in the crying wind?

Be cautious friend for before you now,
Stands the haunted cross of Herbertstown.
'Twas there on high the felons swung,
As the Bean-Ó-Sidhe voice in the silence sung.

Make haste, all haste to Holycross,
For fear your soul from God is lost.
For here be ghosts that evil bring,
'Tis Bean-Ó-Sidhe cry o'er the howling wind.

We're near the town of ancient Bruff,
Pause and pray as sweet waters rush.
Is it the Morning Star singing a dirge,
Or the Bean-Ó-Sidhe cry the long night fill?

Desmond Castle is black and bleak,
As in its dungeons foul demons shriek.
Pray God this night to forgive your sins,
As the Bean-Ó-Sidhe glides past Pallas Green.

Lough Gur appears in ghostly light
'Adieu' Good friend this solemn night.
For here I leave you, for here I sleep,
I was your host, the Bean-Ó-Sidhe.

Louie Byrne

CASTLE FORBES

'A rope, a rope, to hang the Pope
A piece of cheese to toast him.
A barrel of beer to drink his health
And a right good fire to roast him.

In the far off days of which I write there was great animosity between the Irish and the landed gentry. On one side there were the Irish Catholics and on the other the Protestant order. My Sean Scéal relates to the Earl Granard of Lough Forbes....

On the shore of Lough Forbes stood Castle Forbes, the seat of the Earl of Granard. A high defensive wall surrounded the estate. Inside the estate was an ancient graveyard where the Irish had a right to inter their dead. That was until the earl decided in 1800 that he would no longer tolerate the Irish trespassing on his estate. There would be no more Irish burials in the old graveyard. To add insult to injury he forbade them to ever enter the graveyard again. The Irish ignoring this callous order continued to visit the graves of their loved ones and to inter those who died in their family plots. This act of defiance irritated his lordship so much that he ordered that the graves be levelled. Any new interments were to be dug up and despatched over the wall of the estate. Following this callous act he instructed his bailiffs to shoot on sight anyone found trespassing on his land. In the village lived an old man named Pat Slattery, the last of his clan. His family and his family before him were buried in the old graveyard.
"I am determined that when I die, I will be buried in the family plot come what may." He swore. The old man could be seen daily, leaning on his blackthorn stick beside the wall separating him from the family vault.
What anger he felt could be seen plainly in his old eyes.
"I'll be laid to rest in our family vault in spite of you and your cronies." He would shout over the wall hoping for his lordship to hear him.
Time passed and old Pat was now too weak to take the long road to the estate wall.

149

"Place my bed facing the old graveyard so that I may continue to pray for my family." He requested. Dutifully his neighbours carried out the old man's request.

On a summer's day in the year 1805 a neighbour came as was usual with a bowl of broth to his room. Slumped in the bed the old man let out a sigh.

"Come nearer and listen to me." He pleaded.

"What is it Pat, are you not well?" The neighbour held his hand.

"My time has come, would you ever send for the priest and the neighbours." That afternoon they assembled around his bedside and awaited his last wishes.

"Listen carefully now, when I am gone I want you to bury me in my family vault." He pleaded.

The neighbours looked at each other in disbelief. How could old Pat Slattery ask them to carry out such a dying request? They would be duty bound by a solemn deathbed request. Should they disobey his death wish then his soul would not rest.

"Place my old blackthorn stick in my right hand and at the dead of night bury me in the family vault. Swear to me that you will carry out my instructions, that I may rest in peace." He looked at each and everyone in the room in turn. They had little choice in the matter.

Old Pat on hearing their willingness to carry out his last request, slowly rested back on his pillow and with a smile on his face died peacefully.

Following the three day wake the coffin was sealed. Then at the dead of night it was taken to the little graveyard inside the estate and interred.

The burial of old Pat remained a secret within the village for sometime. That was until...

The earl when walking through his estate stumbled upon the newly opened vault of the Slattery clan. Enraged he ordered that the vault be opened and the coffin thrown over the wall.

That night there was a great wailing and crying in the village. Blessing themselves the neighbours ran to the shelter of their homes. The Bean-Ó-Sidhe could be heard lamenting in the old graveyard.

"Whatever can be the matter, is the old earl dead?" They looked with trepidation towards the estate.

Next day they knew the reason when they found the coffin of old Pat lying on the rocks outside the estate. Through the side panel they saw his old blackthorn stick. What were they to do? Digging a hole they buried the coffin as near to the old graveyard as the wall would allow. That night there was again a disturbance in the village. The ghost of old Pat was seen hobbling on his stick towards the estate.

It was midnight when the earl was disturbed by a presence in his bedchamber. Rising, he took his flint and lit the candle. From under his pillow he took his loaded flintlock.

"Who is there, show yourself?" He challenged.

He heard the tap-tap of a stick approaching, his gun shook in his hand. The cold hand of fear filled the room as a mist arose from a dark recess.

"In God's name show yourself, I'm armed and will shoot." He warned.

Slowly the mist moved towards him, he began to shiver. Shadows danced across the room then...

From out of the shadows came the ghost of old Pat Slattery dressed in his rotting burial shroud. Lifting his blackthorn stick he slowly approached. The earl looked in terror at the spectre standing before him.

"Where did you come from, speak in Gods name man, who are you?"

"To you my name matters not, my rightful resting place does. You stole and defiled that right, condemning me to wander this earth. This night you will answer for that crime."

"Rights! What are you talking about? I am Lord of all these lands. You do not frighten me pretending to be a ghost." Showing his bravado he faced Pat. The earl primed his gun and pointing it at the ghost of old Pat fired. The bullet passed through the spectre. Dropping the gun he clutched his heart and fell to the floor.

Next morning the servants went to the locked door and called to their master. Unable to get a reply and worried for his health they broke the door open. They found him lying dead on the floor, his discharged gun beside him. An old blackthorn stick was lying by his side. A bullet was embedded in the panelled wall.

His dead eyes were open in terror and on his lips a silent scream.

THE DYING POET

When my time is come and life has been,
To lie beneath the sod with eyes unseen;
Open the pages of these my books,
Remember me when you take a look.

On these pages I tell Sean Scéals,
But now my life has really failed.
I pray to God for another while,
Before I'm buried in the soil.

There's many the tale I've yet to tell,
Before the sexton rings that bell.
Perhaps it's best I tell them not;
For the story line I've quiet forgot.

Ah! Reader now, your prayers I seek,
For me, your author so humble and meek,
Come open the pages and forget me not,
For little time on earth I've got.

Did you not hear the Bean-Ó-Sidhe cry?
And the Clúracháns at my window sigh?
Three gentle knocks at the door I gave,
Before I departed for my earthly grave.

In the Astral world of Tír-na-nÓg,
My spirit now in freedom roams,
Weep not for me in grief and pain,
At Leac-na-Uaisge we'll meet some day.

Louie Byrne©

THE MIRACLE

(A TWO ACT PLAY)

'If... Silence sits and silence waits,
The troubled mind it not forsakes;
If...My past I could but alter,
And my present life but barter,
My troubled mind it would not brood,
As pheasants do in open woods.
If... Diana the Goddess of light,
Would shroud her light in the clouds of night.
Then the mice and the voles would forage freely
With no fear of the soft winged owl screeching.
If...is a word that has no meaning,
For me or you with little reason.'

Mary Slattery, the local nurse, come dogsbody came to attend to the needs of Gregory Duff. He had taken a bad turn and felt that he was at Deaths door but not according to Mary. She was used to his hypochondriac callings. On this occasion he felt really bad and insisted that she send for the Priest.

"Thank you for calling, Father. I want to speak to you private like."
Greg supported by his elbows rose from his pillow and moaned on seeing the Priest in the doorway.

"Mary would you leave us and don't let anyone into the room." The Priest gently closed the door behind her.

"Now Greg my son, do you want me to hear your confession?"

"No father not as such, but I do have a request."

"I'm all ears, now what is it?" The Priest sat down beside the bed.

"You know father that when the Pope dies they hit him on the head with a hammer?

"You're not rambling in the head, my son?" The Priest looked concerned.

"Not at all father, I'm as sane as yourself. I want you to do for me as they do for his holiness when I die. Not asking too much,am I?"

"No! I was just wondering why you would want to be hit on the head with a hammer?" The Priest scratched his head.

153

"I read somewhere that when the Pope dies they hit him on the head three times with a hammer and ask him each time if he's dead."
"I've never heard the likes, why would they want to do that?"
"To make sure that he had gone to Heaven. Then they would be free to elect a new Pope. They couldn't have two Popes on earth, don't you understand"
"If someone hit him on the head with a hammer three times, then of course he would be dead." The good priest looks puzzled.
"No Father! They ask him if he is really dead. If he answers then they know he's alive but if he remains silent they know that he has gone to Heaven. See what I mean?" Greg tries to explain himself.
"What in God's holy name are you blabbering about? If I hit you on the head with a hammer do you know what would happen?"
"No father you still don't understand me. When they hit him with the hammer and he doesn't answer then they know he is in Heaven. That's why I want to be hit with the hammer so as to get straight to Heaven too. Get my meaning now? By the way what would happen to you if you tapped me with a hammer?"
"I'd be up before the court for murder, that's what."
"No father you still don't understand, they use a silver hammer and hit him gently on the forehead." You don't have to worry about what the law would say or do, I couldn't complain, wouldn't I be dead before you tapped me with the hammer?"
"Now Greg put that notion out of your mind. Where would I get a silver hammer from and secondly I have no intention of doing any such a thing? Mind you sometimes you'd test the patience of a saint."
"You wouldn't need to use a silver hammer you could use the coal hammer and give me gentle taps. If I were alive I could let you know."
"In God's name what's wrong with you. Have you lost the little sense that you were born with? I told you that it's out of the question, hitting you with a hammer indeed, whatever next? Now is there anything else?"
"Like the Pope, I too have a great fear of being buried alive. If you won't hit me with the hammer then would you cut my wrists open?"
"For the last time, No! Put any such notion out of your head. The doctor will know when you have died. Have no fear on that score."
"But father..."
"Forget it, now if there's nothing else? I'm very busy."

"If they can do it for the Pope why cannot you do it for me? I'll pay you." Greg insisted.

"I told you to forget it. However I'll ask the Bishop if what you tell me is true, then I'll let you know what he says. Will that satisfy you?"

"I'm ever so grateful father. If he says that you can hit me with a hammer will you do it, please?"

"If it will console you and the Bishop agrees then I'll give you a gentle tap. How's that?"

"Thank you Father. Don't forget now three taps but not too gentle I may be sleeping. You could give me a shake as well."

"Mary you can come in now." The Priest let out a sigh and opened the bedroom door.

"How is he Father?

"Sure he'll see us all out. The ould mind is rambling a bit but otherwise he's in good form."

"That ould Devil, may God forgive me will be the death of me. He has no more hope of reaching the pearly gates than you and I, father." She informed the Priest without thinking.

"Mary! What a thing to say and you such a charitable woman? Still listening to him I cannot really blame you." The good Priest chided her.

"Forgive me father, but that man would drive a saint to sin, so he would."

"You're forgiven Mary but in future hold that tongue of yours."

"I'll not be able to call on himself to morrow, that is if he's still with us." She looked down at Gregory groaning in the bed.

"I hope that you are not sour with me for chastising you, Mary?"

"Not at all, father. I have to attend to Mrs Maloney. Her new baby is due to morrow. There's always his daughter Breda. I know that she's a bit slow in the head but she's sensible enough to call on the doctor should the need arise."

"Very well Mary, he's in God's hands and will need all his help with Breda looking after him. By the way if he mentions anything regarding a hammer... Oh! never mind just ignore him."

"Not a very charitable remark, father, if I might say so? What's this about a hammer?" Mary looked puzzled.

"You wouldn't understand." The Priest shook his head.

Breda cycled to the surgery of Doctor Flynn who lived some five miles away in a distant village. Once there she gave her diagnostic account of his illness.

"That's enough for me to be getting on with." The doctor called as Breda continued to exaggerate how ill her father really was. The doctor harnessed the pony and made all haste to the bedside of Gregory Duff.

On opening the door he was confronted by his patient snoring on a settled bed beside a roaring turf fire.

"Wake up man, why the urgency of the call? Whatever is the matter with you?" He shook the old man awake.

"Wha! What do you mean cannot you let me die in peace?" Greg rubbed the sleep from his eyes.

"What ails you, man?" The doctor pulled down the lid of Greg's right eye and looked deep inside.

"It's not me eye you old fool, it's me innards. Me belly keeps rumbling something awful. It keeps going round and round and giving me the most awful wind." Greg rubbed his belly and let off a series of farts. "See doctor, that's me problem."

The doctor stood back to let the air clear then he examined Greg's tongue and took his pulse. Placing his stethoscope on the chest of his patient he continued with the examination tapping his chest in the process. Sitting back on the bed he removed the stethoscope and looked down at his patient and shook his head.

"Tell me doctor am I about to meet my maker?" Greg groaned.

"Some day we all will have to." Replied the doctor.

"I'm serious doctor. You can tell me I've made my peace and I'm ready to die. Did the Priest mention anything about a hammer?"

"Not unless you have a need to. A hammer! No I don't understand, why would he mention a hammer?"

"He's going to hit me with one just to make sure that I'm dead."

"Indeed! I'll not ask why he should do such a deed."

At this news old Greg's smiled and relaxed back on the pillow.

"That news seems to have cheered you up better than a tonic. I'll give you a prescription for your problem. Get Breda to fetch it from the chemist and cut down on the bacon and cabbage." The doctor advised.

"Thanks be to God for that doctor. I knew that he wouldn't be so unkind." Greg smiled.

"Whatever makes you say that Greg?"

"You know full well doctor that my brother Gerald is three years older than me and that he should go first, it's only fair."

"If you say so Greg, if you say so." Closing his portmanteau the doctor left.

Next day found Breda again at the doctor's door.

"Whatever now? Don't tell me that he had a relapse?" The doctor asked.

"No doctor but the ould fool won't take his medicine and I'm concerned."

"Don't worry so. Go to the public house and buy a small bottle of brandy and put some into his medicine." The doctor advised.

"Couldn't do that, father is a pioneer. Not a drop has crossed his lips since the night of the mission when he took the pledge. If he found out that I was feeding him brandy he would kill me for sure."

"Seeing that it is for medicinal purposes I see no harm in putting it in his tea with the medicine. What he doesn't know won't worry him." Advised the doctor.

"Where are you off to now Breda?" The neighbours called as she danced down the street.

"Me father has taken bad and I'm going to fetch his medicine." Breda replied and then began to laugh.

"Why are you laughing when your father is so ill?"

"That's a secret between me and the doctor, so it is."

Breda ran down the village street laughing all the way as she was prone to do. This was characteristic of her and for this the villagers were of the opinion that she was' not the full shilling.' There is little doubt but that ubiquitous smile had something to do with what was passing through her childish mind. After all are not pessimists in the habit of labelling all cheerful persons as fools?

ACT TWO

Breda purchased a pint of brandy from Brady's public house and returned to her father's cottage. She hid the bottle and prepared a light meal for him as suggested by the good doctor.

"What in God's name is this swill? They ate better during the great hunger." *Her father stuck his spoon in the stirabout and looked disgusted.*

"Eat it up father, it's for you own good." *His daughter advised.*

"Good! I'd rather be dead. Here go and make me a sup of tae."

She laughed to herself as she watched her father take a deep draught of what he thought was tea.

"This tastes funny and is very strong. Whatever is in it?" *Again he took a deep draught and smacked his lips. After a few more deep slugs the mug was empty. He again paused and licked his lips. Then he let out a roar that would do justice to a bull on heat.*

"Jesus, Mary and Holy Saint Joseph." *Spluttering and choking he threw the mug followed by the bowl of stirabout across the room. Holding his throat he sat staring at the opposite wall. Jumping out of the bed he fell to his knees and reaching under the pillow retrieved his rosary beads.*

"Hail Mary full of grace." *He began praying aloud.*

Breda ran to a corner of the room and falling to her knees began praying with her father. Rising he looked with fire in his eyes at his daughter.

"It's the end of me Breda, why did you poison me?" *Where is the hammer? Placing it over his shoulder he staggered towards her. Collapsing in a heap on the floor he began to mumble prayers.*

Seeing her chance she opened the top half of the half door and without stopping to open the lower half she jumped over it like a steeplechaser and in the process scattered the hens that were scratching outside the door. Up the street she ran shouting that her poor father had gone mad and died.

Mary Slattery looked up from the bedside of Molly Maloney in shock, as she was in the middle of delivering her child. The door was flung opened and in rushed Breda and pulled her away from the bedside.

"Mary! Mary will you come at once father went raving mad and I think he is dead. He was looking for the hammer to kill me with it."

She pulled at Mary's skirt. In the process Mary's skirt came away leaving her in a state of disarray, her petticoat torn.

"Let go of me, can't you see that Molly is about to give birth? If as you claim that your father is dead, then there is nothing that I can do. I cannot work miracles." She tried to release herself from Breda's vice like grip and at the same time cover her modesty.

"My baby is coming. Mary please come and help?" Cried Molly as she saw the baby's head appearing.

"Hold on Molly wait for me. I'm doing my best but I cannot handle two of you. Don't move until I get rid of this one." Mary cried out as she felt herself being strangled by Breda's vice like grip.

Having finally released herself from Breda, Mary returned to the task of delivering the baby but it was too late.

"Has the whole world gone mad?" Molly sat in a trance looking down at the newborn infant.

Having seen to Molly and her baby Mary crossed to where Breda was kneeling over a chair praying for the soul of her father.

"Father is dead and I killed him." She wailed between prayers.

"Killed him, whatever are you blabbering about? Come back to the cottage and we'll soon find out what this is all about?" Mary put her shawl round her shoulders and escorted her to her father's cottage.

On arrival at the cottage they were met by a sight for sore eyes. The old man lay on the dirt floor naked as the day he was born. He had the coal hammer in one hand and his rosary in the other. Between prayers he kept shouting... "It's not fair, it's not fair."

"What's not fair and for God's sake show some shame and cover yourself?" Mary chided the old man. Between them they managed to get him back into the bed.

"Best fetch the doctor, Breda." Mary advised.

"No! Not the doctor, I'm too near death for his help. Send for the Priest and my eldest brother for I must talk with them."

"Very well go fetch your uncle and hurry before it's too late, there's a good girl." Mary pushed her gently towards the door.

Breda returned to the cottage with uncle Gerald in tow together with the parish priest. Gerald was a wizened old man with tobacco stained whiskers. On his head was a battered old caubeen that had seen better days. His ancient coat dragged along the ground carrying more dung in its wake than a cow with the skutters. Under his right arm he

159

carried a shellaigh and by its size could be construed as a lethal weapon.

"What's up with you now? He grumbled as he poked his brother with his shellaigh.

"What's up? I'll tell you what's up, I'm going to die before you and that's not fair, is it? Oh merciful Jesus my poor head." At this remark his brother removed his caubeen out of respect to the Holy name only to replace it immediately.

"Ah! Let's hope so, amen." Prayed uncle Gerald.

"You hope so do you? Why can't you go first, you're older than me? There's no justice and he won't use the hammer." Groaned Greg as he pointed an accusing finger at the priest.

"It's the will of the Almighty, praise be his holy name. What's this about a hammer?" His brother asked.

"He wants me to hit him three times with the coal hammer after he dies." The Priest informed him.

"It's not fair, it's not fair at all. Oh my poor head, the room keeps spinning round and round." Again wailed Greg.

" Why do you want the Priest to hit you with the coal hammer, I don't understand? Why did you bring me here? Is there something you want me to have before you go?" Uncle Gerald looked puzzled.

"Come to think of it, there is that. It's Breda if you must know."

"Breda! That amadan is that all you intend leaving me?"

"No Gerald I'm not giving her to you. I want you to see her married off before you die. I know that it will be hard on you to find her a husband so I'm leaving her two hundred pounds to which you will add an equal amount. That should find her a husband of sorts."

"You send for me to give you two hundred pounds towards marrying off your daughter, is that it? What of the cottage and the land?"

"That will go with her to sweeten her new husband, you've nobody to leave your farm to, she may as well have it as anyone else. Shure who in his senses would marry my daughter if she had no inheritance?"

"Let me get this straight you want two hundred pounds and my farm settled on your daughter just because she is not the full shilling. The man to take her on would want to be a fool like herself to take that one on."

"May God forgive you Gerald Duff?" Mary chided the eldest brother.

"It's only right Gerald seeing that you have no heir. She should be seen to." Intervened the parish priest.
"Please Gerald promise me that you will see to it that Breda gets a good husband before you go? The Priest is to get fifty Pounds if he uses the hammer."
"Are you stark raving mad?" Gerald stroked his whiskers and looked down at his brother.
"He's not or so he claims. He says that when the pope dies he is hit with a hammer... Oh God! Now he has me at it." The Priest blessed himself.
"Very well Greg we'll forget the hammer. I was going to leave my will in favour of the parish priest but seeing that his reverence thinks that she should have the lot then so be it. I promise on your deathbed that before I go I'll see to it that she is properly wed. You'll have to sort out the hammer job yourself, that's between you and the good Priest. Satisfied?"
"Now don't be too hasty Gerald. I didn't mean to settle your whole estate on Breda. There's plenty to allow a little leeway. We mustn't forget the mother church now must we?" The Parish Priest on hearing this conversion intervened.
"No father! Sorry but it's too late. I made this promise on my brothers death bed and I'll not renege on it." Gerald confirmed.
"Done! Give me your hand on it and I'll forgive you for not going to Heaven first. Now my mouth is as dry as a lime kiln would there be a sup of tae left?" Greg somehow revived and relieved at the agreement reached out his hand, which his brother took. The deal was struck there and then. Breda filled the mug with tae and handed it to her father.
"The tae still tastes funny and is real strong, real strong indeed." Draining the mug over his head Greg licked his lips and lay back in the bed.
Then he took a fit of violent praying before tossing the mug across the room. Jumping out of the bed and he as naked as the day he was born he passionately embraced Mary much to her embarrassment. The parish Priest grabbed the hammer and ran to a corner before covering his eyes.
"Get him off me the randy git?" Mary pleaded as Greg dragged her towards the bed.

Mary finally released herself from Greg's embrace and adjusted her attire.

"Get hold of him Gerald, hold him down before he gets too violent."
The priest held his large crucifix before his face and repeatedly blessed himself. Gerald raising his shellaigh crowned his brother with it. He immediately slumped to the floor dragging Mary's skirt off in the process. The priest again ran to a safe corner and turning his back he blessed himself repeatedly.

"Give me a drop of that tae?" Called Mary as she regained her composure and retrieved her modesty.

Taking a delicate sip from the mug she paused and looked across at Breda.

"What is this? It's not tae at all, why its pure brandy. Little wonder that the poor man was violent and raving, he's as drunk as a skunk." She called as she again put the mug to her lips.

"What did you put in the Tae Breda?" The priest asked.

"The doctor told me to put the brandy in the tae with the medicine. I done as he told me." She looked down at her uncle holding his brother tightly.

"Why he's drunk out of his head, so he is." Releasing his grip on his brother Gerald smelt his breath and putting his shellaigh under his arm stamped out of the room. He paused at the cottage door and looked back in at the gathering.

"All promises are off, I assure you. Get your daughter married off yourself; she's your responsibility." Stamping his feet he walked down the road muttering to himself.

"I done nothing wrong. I only done what I was told." Pleaded Breda as she wiped her nose on her sleeve.

"You're a good girl, what happened here is God's holy will. I must be off now and have a few words with that uncle of yours." The priest picked up his hat and was last seen running down the road after Uncle Gerald. Breda stood in the doorway with the teapot in her hand. She was smiling as they challenged Uncle Gerald to return.

That was our Breda forever the optimist. Like the Mona Lisa that ubiquitous smile somehow related to the situation in hand. After all, pessimists are in the habit of thinking that all smiling persons are fools for not appreciating the miseries of life.

THE FAT LADY SINGS

NIGHTMARE

I dreamed one night of howling ghosts,
Of uninvited shadowy hosts.
My sleep disturbed, I tossed in fear,
What did it mean, what could it be?

The leaves were torn from the trees,
They turned to ghosts and attacked me.
My hands I held across my face,
From their savage attack I tried to escape.

In panic blind through woods I raced,
To escape the onslaught, my feet I paced.
Screaming branches clawed at me,
Their hair I caught, they tore it free.

Screeching owls and moaning ghosts,
Treated me as if their host.
Reaching up their wings I trapped,
In downy feathers my hands I wrapped.

I heard them scream 'let go of me,'
As with a kick they broke free.
'Wake up, you fool'? My wife did call
Pull any more hair and I'll soon be bald.

LOUIE BYRNE©

163

THE LITTLE RED BOAT
Lost Opportunity

'Opportunity knocks on every door:
Or so we're often told,
I question did it knock for me?
That is why a sage I seek,
To come and rap upon my door,
And explain to me the reason why.
Opportunity it passed me by'?
What's left but tears and mournful sighs?'

LOUIE BYRNE©

On a dark night Christmas Eve on a country road from Foynes to Limerick Ireland the story unfolds...

The driver, on his way home from his family home in Kerry looked out in trepidation at the fog as it ebbed and flowed. He had spent an enjoyable week on his yacht moored in Ballybunion Bay. This he had purchased from funds left to him when still a child in the will of an anonymous benefactor. To add to his discomfort the night was as dark as a raven's wing. The cold mist coming off the Shannon River hung in a thick veil obliterating his vision.

"Thank God the road is empty." He prayed as he coaxed the car towards the village of Patrick's well. The dawn was breaking as he approached the village. It came as a shock and surprise on seeing the silhouette of a tall man sheltering under a whitethorn bush. He was cautious and suspicious of this stranger. Should he continue on his journey, ignoring the stranger or stop and offer his help, should it be asked? His mind was in a quandary and he was apprehensive as he came level with the stranger. Bringing the car to a halt he rolled down the window.

"My name is Father Edmond Dillon. Can I be of assistance?" He called into the night.

"Thank you very much father, you are kind." An elderly gentleman hobbled from under the sanctuary of the bush. Rubbing his hands together he rounded the car and entered by the passenger door.

"Been long on the road, if you don't mind me asking?" The driver asked by way of conversation.

"On the road, did you say? A long time a very long time indeed. Still the wait was worth it." The stranger looked out into the swirling mist. The driver thought this a very strange remark but decided to ignore it. On the road they continued to hold a very genial conversation. His wit and humour making the journey all the more comfortable.

"I'd like to tell you a little story, that is if you have the patience to listen?" The stranger sprung this surprise.

"Fire away my friend sure we have all the time in the world." The driver retorted.

"It all happened a long time ago you must understand. Christmas Eve it was. Come to think of it, it happened on this very night, many years ago. It all came about in the parish of Saint Mary's in the city of...'

"Now there's a coincidence I come from the parish myself. Perhaps I heard the story. You see I'm from...' The driver interrupted.

"Would you please show me the courtesy of listening? I've waited a long time to relate the story to you. Thank you!" The gentleman stopping the driver in mid sentence curtly replied.

"I am sorry, please continue." The driver was taken aback.

"In the parish lived an elderly gentleman, he had neither kit nor kin. A loner some people would say. There was one polite lad that he had taken a liking to by the name of Edmond. The boy became a regular visitor to the cottage to attend to the needs of the old gentleman. Whenever there was a bit of shopping needed or a paper to fetch then Edmond was on hand. In return the gentleman would reward him with a few pence. As time passed the old gentleman became housebound and became more and more dependant on the youth.

On the morning of Christmas Eve Edmond came to the cottage. He was shocked to see that the old man had deteriorated so much. The cottage was ice cold for there was no fire in the grate.

"Please don't be frightened of me son, I'm still your old friend. I now need your helping hand more than ever." The old man noticing the reluctance of the youth to come forward held out a feeble hand of encouragement. His hand shook from the cold.

"Is there something that you want?" Edmond slowly approached the bedside and looked down at the old man.

"This is the last time that I will seek your help son. Take this money to the Parish priest and ask him to say a mass for the repose of my soul? What money I've left is for you, you have been a good boy and a

faithful friend. Now please go and thank you." The youth felt the cold of death as the old man clasped his hand in his. Looking nostalgically after the youth he raised his feeble hand in a final salutation and then collapsed on to the pillow. His strength now exhausted.

"Don't forget to return Edmond. I won't forget you, please don't disappoint me. Promise me you won't forget." He pleaded but the youth was long gone. There was a deafening silence within the car as the passenger paused and looked deep into the driver's eyes as if relating a message.

"Please don't stop, tell me the outcome." Unable to stand the tension the driver pleaded.

"This is where I must leave you." The elderly gentleman called for the car to stop outside the cemetery of Mount Saint Lawrence. Opening the car door he vanished into the morning mist.

"Good luck, we'll meet again please God then you can tell me the ending of the yarn. Merry Christmas to you, I don't think." The driver disappointed at not hearing the conclusion of the story sarcastically called into the mist. Turning left the driver took the road into John's Street in the city of Limerick. Approaching the old bridge he saw the squat tower of Saint Mary's Cathedral rise up from the mist. It was at this point that he remembered who the gentleman was that he encountered under the old whitethorn bush outside the village of Patrickswell in the County Limerick that cold winters night...

It was no co-incidence.

The boy, as he remembered had his heart set on purchasing a little red tin boat that sat in the window of Lena Carr's store in Francis Street Limerick. Daily he would pass up the street to assure himself that the boat was still there. Looking longingly and covetously he would press his face to the window and stroke the glass that separated him from his goal...The Little Red Boat'. It would break his little heart if someone else purchased that boat before he could raise the money to buy it. He knew that he could never afford to buy it, yet he lived in hope. Passing the window that Christmas Eve morning with the donation for the mass held tightly in his hand he paused and looked into the window.

He was shocked to see the hand of the proprietor removing his little red boat. His young heart missed a beat... His boat was sold!

"What are you doing with my boat?" He cried in an agitated state as he pushed the door open and entered the shop.

"Your boat son? Show some manners or leave at once." Lena looked up startled and demanded.

"I'm sorry, really I am. Please! Oh please God don't sell my boat." The boy pleaded through his tears.

"Dry your tears it's not your boat. Anyhow it is not sold yet. A gentleman has paid a deposit and hopes to raise the balance before Christmas."

"A deposit! What's that?" He wiped his snotty nose in the sleeve of his ganzie.

"It means that should he raise the full money then the boat is his. In the meantime should someone come in with the full amount then the boat belongs to him or her? Do I make myself clear?"

"Sufficient amount!" He squeezed the Mass offerings deeper into his sweating palm. He hesitated for a moment before spilling the offerings on to the counter.

"Will this buy my boat?" He pushed the money under the nose of the proprietor. Counting out the money she looked down at the boy.

"You're still sixpence short." She informed him.

"I have that here." Reaching into his pocket he produced the sixpence given to him that morning by poor old Tom. He ran from the shop hugging his precious little red boat to his chest. He wanted to get home and try it out. He no longer had time for old Tom.

That Christmas morning on his way from Mass he saw a small gathering outside old Toms door. Ignoring them and the glass hearse with the four black horses he raced on...

His only interest was sailing his small red boat.

Edmond J Dillon stopped his car outside the door to his presbytery and entered the house.

"Do you want a bite to eat, father?" His housekeeper asked.

"Not now Bridget, I have more pressing business to perform." There were tears in his young eyes and a lump came to his throat as he spoke. Going to his room he searched through his belongings until he found what he was seeking. Dressing in the sacred robes used for celebrating mass for the dead he took down the large iron key to the church door. Walking through the old graveyard he looked up at a watery sun trying to break through the early morning mist. In the

167

distance he saw the old rugged cross lying askew on the neglected grave. Approaching the grave he tried to straighten the cross. There was a loud crack as the base of the rotting cross collapsed.

"Sorry Tom, can you ever forgive a selfish child that loved a 'Little Red Tin Boat' more than his friend? I'll replace your cross as new, I promise. This time I'll not be so selfish nor will I forget." He went to wipe his nose on the sleeve of his robe, he paused as he remembered the day so long ago when a snotty nosed boy wiped his nose in his sleeve as he cried for a little red boat. With tear filled eyes he gently placed the cross on the grave of old Tom.

"This is yours by right, Tom." He removed a battered 'little Red Tin Boat' from his pocket and placed it beside the cross. His heart was breaking and falling to his knees he openly wept. Rising he retreated to his church and placing the old iron key in the lock he pushed the great door open.

"Tom"! He stood aside allowing the spectre free access.

That morning alone with the ghost of Old Tom, Father Edmond J Dillon, newly elected parish Priest of Saint Mary's knelt before the high altar and celebrated the belated mass for the soul of Old Tom, the stranger he met on the road from Ballybunion in the county Kerry. Do you know who his generous benefactor was? Do you care?

Do you know who was the sacristan was that served the Mass with father Edmond Dillon that night...Do you?"

Dedicated To my good friend Edmond Dillon. Solicitor

LIFE'S DREAM

I'm now alone; I feel life's grief,
My faithful dog rests at my feet.
There are no more places left to roam,
I've seen it all. Wild oats I've sown.

In a humble cottage I rest my head,
Remembering the things I done and said.
I've stories to tell of the places I've been,
Sights of the world wonders seen.

Yet who is there or whom to tell,
Of what has been, of the life I led?
The cruel wind cries around my door,
My life's now spent, I'm going home.

Wearily I rise and open the door,
My dog set free, the fields to roam.
Where are they now who made good cheer,
And drank a toast or two with me?

The day is spent night is closing in,
I pray to God to forgive my sins.
A last good bye to you my friends,
My life and dreams are at an end.

Should you find me, look no more,
For the tales I told, the deeds so bold.
Too late are you my absent friend,
Too late alas to make amends.
LOUIE BYRNE ©

O'REGAN'S DAUGHTERS'

A Shepherd lad leaned on his crook,
As o'er his flock he was won't to look.
But other thoughts were on his mind
A bride he sought, a bride to find.

In an age long past it was the custom to auction all land and property that came on to the market. The travelling auctioneer, a man renowned for a canny eye would arrive in the townland and set up his platform. Calling all interested parties to come forward he would lay out his tools of the trade. These consisted of a large ledger, a gavel, a candlestick, a collection of candles and a metal probe.

"This is the marker and here is the six inch candle for all to inspect. At the opening I will insert the probe into the centre of the candle and light it. The bidding will remain open until the flame reaches the probe. When the probe drops from the candle the bidding will come to a halt. Whoever bids last will be deemed to be the purchaser, is that understood?"

My Sean Scéal opens in the village of Ballydehob in the County of Cork where two brothers named Tom and Trevor Kilderry lived with their aged parents. They were as different as chalk and cheese. Tom was a quiet man that kept himself to himself. Trevor! Well he was like the waters of Roaring Bay, as cantankerous a gentleman as one would wish to avoid.

It was when both parents passed on that it happened...

I tell you in all sincerity that a lie would die on my lips. Would I, your Seanachai lie to you? By right of inheritance Tom was now the rightful owner of the farm. Trevor would have none of it.

"I worked the farm too and I'll have my half or else it will have to go to auction." Demanded Trevor. Tom reluctant to see the old homestead go to strangers agreed to leave the farm lot stock and barrel to his younger brother. With the farm legally signed over, he immediately ordered his brother off the farm without one brass farthing.

Tom took up residence in an abandoned cottage deep in the Gabriel Mountains. There he successfully began raising pedigree sheep. His sheep were to become famous throughout the length and breath of Ireland.

On fair days in the town of Skibbereen bidders would vie with each other hoping to purchase some of his fine ewes and rams. Tom was content enough but the cold winters and wet summers were another matter. What he needed and wanted was a girl to keep his back warm on the cold winter nights.

A wife willing to share his small fortune and God willing to give him an heir, to hold an intelligent conversation with round the turf fire. A girl to keep his cottage clean and tidy with a little cooking and baking thrown in. Not a lot to ask, but what girl would marry a shepherd living in a cottage in the mountains? He thought.

Tom heard of a family living outside the village of Skibbereen who had a daughter of marriageable age. Determined not to spend another winter without the comfort of a girl in his bed he set out to meet the matchmaker. Hobbling one of his finest ewes he placed her round his neck and set out to meet the matchmaker who lived the other side of Drishane Bridge.

"Well bless my soul it's yourself Tom Kilderry. Now what brings you to the cottage of the matchmaker, as if I didn't know?" She laughed.

Tom took the sheep from round his neck and opening the spancel allowed her to roam freely.

"I've brought you my finest breeding ewe, Mary Culligan. Could we go inside for the 'Craic'?"

"Come in and welcome Tom and take that coat off if you are staying." Mary stood aside allowing Tom inside.

"God bless the house and all who enter." Tom took the holy water and blessed himself, as was the custom.

"Amen! Thank you Tom." Mary acknowledged the blessing.

"You see I brought you one of my finest ewes, Mary. It shows that my intentions are honourable does it not?" Tom stuttered.

"Tom Kilderry will you be at your ease. Thanks for the sheep it's appreciated. Now would you get to the point?"

"Well Mary it's like this...You know how lonesome a man gets talking to nothing but sheep in the mountains? There is a family living over in Skibbereen who have a daughter of marriageable age. I'm a bit on the

171

*shy side where women are concerned and I'm asking you to do the
calling for me. Would you ever oblige and do that for me?"*
*"Tom! You are one decent man so you are. Sure there was no need to
ask, nor for that matter to bring the sheep. Grateful though I am. I'll
make it my business to go first light to morrow. How does that suit
you?"*
Tom left the house of the matchmaker with a song in his heart.
*Some days later when Tom was in the mountain tending to his sheep
who did he see trundling up the boréen but Mary Culligan?*
*"Tom Kilderry, you'll be the death of me I swear." Mary sat down on
a slab of rock to regain her breath.*
*" Mary! Not bad news is it. Please, you can tell me?" Tom fell to his
knees holding on to his shepherds crook.*
"Why should I bring you bad news, tell me?" Mary looked startled.
"I was wondering because you came back so soon."
*"You give up too easily that's your trouble. Is it little wonder that your
brother took advantage of you? Now before I go any further with the
matchmaking I must tell that there are two daughters. There is a
second party in the bidding, I'll let you know. It's that blackguard of a
brother of yours. I'm informed on good authority that he intends to
have the younger one come what may and to be honest with you I
cannot blame him." This news came as a shock to Tom I can tell you.*
"I was not aware that there were two daughters. Does it matter?"
*"Of course it matters Tom. How naive can you be? Anne is the girl for
you believe me. I fear that the eldest daughter would be the death of
you. However there is nothing that you can do for now. Go to the
auction and bid like everyone else. All I can do is to pray for your
success. I suppose you'll want your ewe back seeing as I've been of
little help?"*
*"No Mary! I gave you that ewe in good faith and you done your level
best. Keep the ewe and may she bring you nothing but good luck."*
*God forgive me but of the two daughters the eldest was beyond belief.
She was as cantankerous as a rusting five barred gate. She had a
tongue as cutting as a barbed wire fence.*
*No dowry no matter how tempting would induce any bachelor with an
ounce of sense to marry her. She was it would appear destined to
remain a spinster or else to join the nuns.*

172

It was said that the milk in the churn would turn sour if she looked at it. A man would have to have a face like the backside of a bull to consider her. Not a very charitable assessment of her I agree.

The younger daughter was as sweet a cailín as ever came out from the County Cork. Suffice to say that it was the second daughter that all the bachelors wanted for a wife.

Tom returned to his home in the mountains and sat down by a babbling brook. He was disappointed and frustrated, but as he said such was the will of the almighty. His trauma was disturbed when he heard a stranger coming down the mountain track singing.

"Good day to your good self Tom Kilderry, what a fine sunny day. May I partake of your spring water?" The stranger asked politely.

"To be sure and welcome. You can have fresh ewe milk if you would prefer." Tom offered.

"That's more than generous and thank you." Tom and the stranger sat on a carraig drinking milk and exchanging gossip.

"Tell me to mind my own business Tom, but why did you never take a wife?" The stranger asked by way of conversation.

"Sure its a sore subject that you bring up this day of all days," Tom leaned heavily on his crook.

"I can see that you are worried Tom and I feel for you. Tell me the whole story I may be of assistance to you."

Tom related the whole story, starting with the loss of the farm.

"Tom! That is indeed a tragic story it touches me ould heart. You tell me that the daughters are to be auctioned to the highest bidder at the fair in Skibbereen, is that so?"

"True enough I did that; but what chance have I a poor sheep farmer? Sure half of Cork and no doubt Limerick too will be there."

"Don't be so hard on yourself Tom Kilderry. There's many the cailín that would welcome the comfort of your feather bed. Rest assured of that. You go to the fair and when you get there this is what you must do. As the candle burns watch it and when the probe begins to fall out then and only then shout out your bid. Not before and not after, now remember my instructions."

"How am I to know which daughter I'm bidding for?"

"That's the crux of the matter for O'Regan of Skibbereen is a clever ould fox. He will not disclose which of his daughters is first for the bidding. You should bet ten finest ewes in lamb. Remember all that I

173

told you and I thank you for your generosity. You might take the courtesy of inviting me to your wedding." Before he could ask him, should he bid on the first or second candle the stranger had vanished? The day of the auction and fair came and the square was packed with people. The auctioneer took his place on the platform and the gathering crushed forward to see the auction for the daughters of O'Regan of Skibbereen. In the meantime Trevor had gone to make a deal with the auctioneers assistant.

"Ten golden sovereigns are yours if you disclose to me when Anne the daughter of O'Regan of Skibbereen is to be auctioned." He offered the bribe to the assistant.

"Ten golden sovereigns is it now? You're a rogue I've no doubt Trevor. Still for that kind of money I'd sell me soul to the Devil himself. Tell you what; I'll hold my hand up high when the little darling comes up for auction. Remember, don't bid until you see me raise my hand." The assistant held out his hand and accepted the bribe.

The auctioneer lit the candle and the bidding commenced. Slowly the candle burnt nearer and nearer to the probe. Trevor watched the assistant nervously.

A little man in a caipean dearg (Red Cap) came behind the rostrum and threw a golden sovereign beside the candle. The greedy assistant saw the coin and rushed up the steps to retrieve it. Reaching up he grabbed the coin. Trevor saw him raise his hand and began bidding.

"Do I hear twenty sovereigns?" The auctioneer looked into the gathering.

"Here! I'll give that." An old man that should be saying his prayers shouted.

"Thirty sovereigns." Shouted Trevor upping the bid.

Tom kept watching the candle burn nearer and nearer the probe. In his excitement he forgot his promise to the fairy and shouted out.

"Ten best ewes in lamb."

"Thank you Tom Kilderry but your brother outbids you."

"Forty sovereigns and two acres of oats." The old man again upped the bid in his desperation for a wife.

"Fifty sovereigns and two acres of best main crop potatoes." Trevor looked at the old man in anger. The gathering clapped in their

excitement for never had so much been offered for a wife in the history of the village.

The assistant tried to attract Trevor's attention but all Trevor was interested in was the prospect of sharing his bed with Anne.

The rumour got round that the auctioneer must surely be auctioning Anne. Trevor heard the rumour and this confirmed it. He would have Anne's hand that day come what may. Tom watched in dismay knowing that he could never outbid his brother.

"It's the will of God that I'm destined to remain a bachelor." He thought.

"Damn it all. Fifty five sovereigns and three acres of finest oats." The old man croaked.

"Sixty gold sovereigns and four acres of best wheat." Shouted Trevor as the probe fell from the candle.

"She's yours, Trevor Kilderry. Come and pay your bid."

The gathering cheered and clapped Trevor on the back. Congratulating him on his achievement. Trevor went to the rostrum and paid the auctioneer. Tom went across to his brother and taking his hand in his congratulated him.

"It's far from over yet Tom, there is always the other daughter. You could do with a woman like Maggy O'Regan." He laughed.

The auctioneer returned to the rostrum and placed a new candle in the holder and set the probe in the centre.

"I'm now going to auction the second daughter of O'Regan of Skibbereen." The gathering began to laugh.

"My brother will have her, won't you Tom?" Trevor sneered as he entered the alehouse.

"I'll bid ten sovereigns." The old man was once again on his feet.

"It's ten sovereigns against you Tom Kilderry. A bargain if ever I saw one." The auctioneer prompted.

Tom remained silent as the candle slowly burnt nearer the probe.

The bidding had reached twenty sovereigns and was more or less stalemate.

The old man stood watching anxiously as the flame burnt nearer to the probe. He was sure that this time he would be lucky.

Tom looked behind the rostrum and saw the fairy waving to him. It was now or never.

175

"Ten finest ewes in lamb." He shouted as the probe fell with a clatter on to the rostrum.

"She's yours Tom Kilderry. Come and pay your bid." The auctioneer called.

The crowd laughed and cheered and sympathised with Tom.

"You'll be a better man for taking her Tom. She'll soon chastise you. Good luck Tom." Trevor held his tankard high and laughed.

That evening Trevor was like a hen on hot eggs as he waited for O'Regan of Skibbereen to bring him his prize.

Hearing a cart trundling up the laneway he rushed to meet his new bride.

"I've brought your new bride Trevor Kilderry and long may you both live and prosper." Opening the door of the cart he led Trevor's new bride out...It was none other than Maggy O'Regan.

"It's her, there's some mistake." Shielding his eyes he ran for the safety of his house. Before he had time to get inside the door Maggy beat him to it and had made herself at home beside the hob.

"Come in and join me Trevor love, we'll make a fine home together." She looked up smiling a toothless grin.

"God help me! Whatever have I let myself in for?" Trevor, in fear and trepidation entered the house.

Meanwhile Tom had returned to his mountain cottage to await his fate.

Who could blame him after all the stories he heard about Maggy O'Regan. He was regretting ever having attended the auction.

He waited in fear and trepidation for the arrival of his bride.

On hearing a commotion in the laneway he was more than apprehensive. To be honest he was shaking like a jelly on a plate. He had made his bed and now he would have to lie in it with Maggy O'Regan.

Taking a deep breath he went out to greet his new bride. Seated on the jaunting car was none other than Anne and she looking for all to see like a rose in full bloom.

"There's some mistake you've brought her to the wrong cottage. She belongs to my brother Trevor." He called as he retreated to his cottage.

"There's no mistake I've brought you your bride, Tom Kilderry." Called the driver raising his whip.

176

"She's mine you say?
But I..". *Tom lost for words looked dumbfounded at the driver.*
"She's yours by right, Tom. Now come here and welcome your bride
to your cottage."
"God love you my little lamb. Come into my arms me darling."
Rushing forward he lifted Anne off the jaunting car and hugged and
kissed her. Carrying her in his arms he entered the cottage. He was
about to close the half door when he looked back at the driver of the
jaunting car.
He looked at the driver in amazement for it was none other than the
little man dressed in green with a caipean dearg on his head.
Tom set his new bride down on the flagged floor then arm in arm they
came to the half door and waved to the driver. With a final farewell
they closed and bolted the door behind them.

The sheep...Well they would have to look after themselves for this day
at least. Tom and Anne had a lot to catch up with.

An Connail na Marb
(The candle of the dead)

'*Four brown candles round his bed*
A halo of primroses on his head.
Four archangels, the prayers have said,
Joseph Kirkin's soul this life has fled'.

I told you time and time again stories of the living, the dead, ghosts and hobgoblins but do you listen? Have you ever visited 'Josephs Rock' in the town of Leenane in the County Mayo and wondered how the rock came to be named? Wonder no more for here I tell another Sean Scéal to make you sit up and take notice...

When one enters this world they are welcomed into it by the light of Coinneal an Solus. (Candle of Light). In Christian times it became known as the Coinneal na Báistead. (Christening Candle) Likewise when one dies they are shown the way back to the other world, the astral world, from whence they came by the Coinneal na Marb (Candle of the dead).

The Sean Scéal I tell is of the occasion when, be it by accident or otherwise, the candle was extinguished before the soul had time to leave for the Astral world...

In the town of Leenane near to Devils Mother Mountain in the County Mayo lived Joseph and Mary Kirkin. They were as happy and devoted a couple as ever came out of the county. Shure why wouldn't they be and they blessed with ten children? Four were boys and six were girls, if you don't be minding. One fine afternoon as Joseph was searching for some lost sheep over by the Twelve Bens Mountains he lost his footing and got trapped between some rocks. By evening he had not returned home and his family became worried for his safety. The landscape around Leenane is vast, wild and rocky and it would take more than their immediate family to organise a search. Calling on their good neighbours to help, a rescue party was soon organised and began a search of the immediate area but without success. When the light began to fail they were forced to abandon the search. Next morning they again took to the hills and resumed the search. By

178

midday there were no results, it was as if the earth had opened up and swallowed him. God between us and all harm.
The good people did not abandon their search. On the third day they found the poor soul. He was dead, his feet trapped in the crevice of a split rock. In time they placed a memorial on the spot that was to become known as 'Joseph's rock'.
The body of Joseph was removed from the mountain on the shoulders of his four sons and taken to the chapel. Next day his body was taken to his home and laid out for the three-day wake. This was the custom of the time in Ireland. Now- a- days it's fancy funeral parlours for our loved ones. In my day one was laid out in their own parlour and rightly so. Say your last farewells to your loved one in the hospitality of their home not in some indifferent so-called funeral parlour. Now I'm getting sentimental and losing track of the story...

At the head of the bed was placed the obligatory blessed Coinneal na MARB. This would give light and guide his soul to the other world when it decided to leave his mortal body. Slowly the candle burnt and flickered throughout the day and night as the mournful wake continued. On the night of the second day of the wake the door to room where the body of Joseph lay was closed. This would allow his soul to prepare itself for its departure before his burial the following day. The window was left partly open should his soul decide to leave during the wake. The assembly gathered in the large kitchen for the final farewell to Joseph Kirkin. All night long they continued the wake leaving Joseph alone with his soul in the back bedroom.
Next morning the coffin was taken to the room and the body placed inside and the lid screwed down. Nobody noticed that the candle had gone out during the night. The coffin was lifted on the shoulders of his four sons and linking arms they took their father to his final resting place in the little cemetery beside the church. With Joseph now at rest the family rallied around to help their mother carry the extra burden of managing the small farm. A week following the burial it was reported that a man looking like Joseph was seen near to the twelve Bens. Little notice was taken of this sighting and soon the incident was forgotten. That was until the Feast of Samain better known as Halloween. The villagers gathered in their church to pray for the

179

repose of their departed relatives and friends. That same night there were several sightings of Joseph. He was seen making his way back to his home in Leenane. Soon the ghost of Joseph Kirkin was seen within the confines of his farm. This was brought to the notice of the Parish priest who decided that Joseph was seeking prayers.

"His soul is wandering the earth seeking our charity." He told the frightened people. Retiring to the church they prayed all the harder that his soul would find rest and return to his grave. All their praying made no difference to the spectre. Day and night it could be seen wandering aimlessly around the farm it was seeking something or someone and could not find eternal rest. They could not fathom out as to why the soul of Joseph would not rest peacefully. As time passed the ghost became more agitated and seemed to be trying to return to its home. His wailing was disturbing the villagers.

"He is looking for someone or something, but what? Would that he found it then he would rest in peace?" Prayed his widow. The priest was called to the farm and exorcise the ghost but without success.

"Whatever is troubling him we must resolve the matter?" The priest informed his flock. The lost ghost continued to wander and wail through the glen and on into the mountains. After many weeks searching it found it's way back into the old farmhouse and to the bedroom where he spent his last hours. He created such distress that the home had to be abandoned. Day and night he could be heard moving about the room and disturbing furniture. His cries were those of a soul in torment.

"Whatever it is that's troubling him is in that room and we must find out what it is?" His widow demanded. In fear and trepidation they returned to the cottage and searched the room. There was nothing in it that would give any clue as to why the dead should want to return. As the others left his widow decided that she would stay behind and say a prayer for his soul. Going into the kitchen she went to the Welsh dresser and opened a drawer. She was about to take out a blessed candle and return to the room when she remembered.

"Come back! Come back all of you." She called. The others looked around at the widow and made all haste back to the cottage.

"What is it Mary, have you found something?"

"I believe I know what the ghost of Joseph is looking for."

"What can it be for we found nothing in the room?"

180

"It is this, the light to guide his soul to the other world. I remember now, but little notice did I take of it at the time. On the morning we removed his corpse the candle was quenched." Mary held up the stump of the Coinneal na Marb for all to see.

"God be good to him, his soul is trapped in that room. Without the light he cannot find the way out to the other world. His poor soul is trapped here on earth." A fresh Coinneal na Marb was obtained from the church and placed in the room. That evening they made sure that the candle was burning brightly before they closed the door leaving the ghost in peace.

From inside the room they heard a gentle sound and falling on their knees began to pray. In fear and trepidation they held a second wake in the kitchen of the old house for the late Joseph Kirkin.

They watched in fear and trepidation as the bedroom door slowly opened and closed. The occupants remained silent, then...

"Jesus, Mary and Saint Joseph protect us this night." An old man prayed. There was an uneasy calm within the room as they again felt a presence cross the floor. Then the main door opened and as it did the candle fluttered. His widow rose and going to the door called out.

"God be good to you Joseph Kirkin, remember us in the next world." A gentle zephyr entered the house and quenched the candle. Closing the door tightly she returned to the gathering and waited.

They waited and they waited, would they come?

They kept looking towards the door. Then it happened...

The three knocks on the door to tell them that the soul of Joseph Kirkin was making his last call. They listened as the Bean-Ó-Sidhe crying her lament accompanied his spirit across the Devil Mountain. He was returning to the astral world from whence he came. They watched and prayed as a single star crossed the horizon.

Next day Mary and her family went to the graveyard and kneeling laid a bunch of primroses and thyme on the grave of the late Joseph Kirkin.

"Rest in peace Joseph." His widow cried.

"Amen." Repeated her children.

All that remains now of this story is 'Joseph's Rock'. His soul has long since found its way back to the spirit world.

The Matchmaker
A Three-Act-Play

ACT ONE

Curtain opens in the home of Greg and Breda Duff

Louie Byrne the matchmaker from Limerick was called upon to refer a match between the families of Slattery and Duff living in the County Clare.

Pat and Mary Slattery had a daughter ready for the nuptial bed and their neighbour Gregory Duff Senior had a son also eligible. A fine match you might think but that was not the way marriages were made in the old days. The matchmaker would have to be called upon... However they did not want nosey neighbours delving into their affairs and for that reason they choose the matchmaker from Limerick.

Louie knew that his reputation depended on the outcome of this arrangement. Clare folk could be canny at the best of times, why else did they go outside the county to find a matchmaker?

The matchmaker met with both families at different times and interrogated them as to what each had to offer. He had a lot of searching and probing to do before he was satisfied as to what each side had to offer the other. You may ask about love? Love! That never came into the equation nobody in his or her right mind would ask about love. *'Love never boiled a pot or put the grub on the table.'* Would come the answer.

There was of course the question of age and how large was the dowry on offer compared with the size of the farm and how many beasts were on the land. The matchmaker had to take all these points into consideration.

Louie met Greg in the family home to discuss the merits of his son.

"Hallo Gregory, I suppose I can call you Greg? It's good to meet a man from a neighbouring county." Louie held out his hand.

Greg looked him up and down and thought to himself... 'What kind of a dandy is this?" Louie was dressed in a fancy waistcoat and top hat.

In his hand he held a silver topped cane and a timepiece hung from the pocket of his waistcoat. No doubt he'll want a good fee?' Greg was having second thoughts.

Louie held Greg's hand, the hand of a hard working farmer. This was an honest man who spent little on himself and no doubt had a good farm and a better bank balance. On his pole was a cap that seen better days and his breeches were tied at the knees with twine. On his feet he wore a pair of Wellington boots and by the looks of them he came to the conclusion that he slept with them on. Greg unable what to make of the matchmaker stood open-mouthed looking at him.

"Are you right Greg, say something?"

"I'm fine, honest, Call me Greg if that's what you wish."

"I see, Greg it is. Now let me know what's on offer here so that I can approach the second party honestly." Looking puzzled at his client Louie removed a notepad from his inside pocket. Then he removed a fancy fountain pen and stood waiting. It was important that he had all the facts before he assessed what the dowry should be.

"Before we go any further, I've had a long journey and my throat is parched. I take it that the good woman of the house has lain on refreshments? An apple pie wouldn't go amiss, I'm sure." Louie sat down in the nearest chair.

"Breda! Would you wet the sup of tae, there's a good girl." Greg addressed his wife.

"Tae is it? Over in Limerick something a little stronger is usually offered, on an occasion such as this, if you get my meaning. However if tae is all that's on offer in Clare... Cromwell was right after all." The matchmaker grumbled.

"Forget the tae Breda, bring the jug and scone." Greg instructed.

"I suppose you'll soon be ready to start?" Greg asked as Louie scoffed the last of the Pie.

"Don't mind me. Fire away Greg, I'm all ears." Removing a red handkerchief from his pocket Louie wiped his chin. The jug of 'Poteen' he placed on the floor between his legs.

"My son, my only son." Gregory senior put emphasis on the word only, will inherit a fine farm of land when God calls us both. There's a fine two-storied slated house and more barns and outhouses than I could count.

A fine young hairy bull of a man is my son. Raring to go like a bull on heat, God bless him. A good Catholic to boot as the Parish Priest will confirm. A regular participant at the altar rails every morning without fail. A son that we are proud of and without a blemish on his character. The matchmaker took notes and listened as Greg continued pouring accolades his only son.

"Tell me Greg why did you send for me?" Louie looked over at Greg.

"Wha! What do you mean, are you not the matchmaker from Limerick?" He stuttered.

"There's no question about that, but from the way you describe your son I thought you might be of the opinion that I was a recruiting Priest from Maynoot College and looking to have him in the Priesthood. Sorry my mistake."

"There's no need to be so sarcastic. I'm stating the facts." Grumbled Greg.

"He's only pulling your leg, Greg." Another piece of pie, Louie?" Breda approached the matchmaker carrying a steaming pie. She genuflected in front of Louie before retreating back to the *leaba suidheachan. (Settled bed used as a sofa by day)*

"For God's sake Breda, he's only a matchmaker not the Pope." Greg grumbled on seeing his wife genuflecting before the matchmaker.

"Well now we had best walk the land before we lose the light." Louie picked up the jug and left the cottage.

"The trap is over yonder, I'll go and fetch it." Greg volunteered.

"No need for that, the walk will do us both good. Now first things first let's see what sort of a farm you have here?" Opening the gate Louie entered the first field and studied the surroundings. After looking into every nook and cranny they returned to the house.

"Well what do you think?" Breda once again had the refreshments ready.

"I must admit that you have a fine farm and a better table." Louie sat down and eyed the well-laden table.

"Now there's the question of the first party, your son. Is he in good health and has he got all his teeth? Then there's the question of his age. What I mean is will he be able to perform?" The matchmaker looked from husband to wife.

"Has he got all his teeth and can he perform. Perform! Perform what might I ask. Are we talking about my son or a bull on heat? Jesus help us what sort of a question is that? Spittle formed on Greg's mouth."

"Come on now no need to upset yourself, here take a drop of this. Is his tackle in order? The party of the second party might be broody. Wouldn't do to find out too late that he couldn't perform on the wedding night, now would it?"

"I can tell you here and now that my son will be more than a match for any broody girl. I know your little game you are on the make for the extra luck penny should he put a bun in the oven?" Greg stood up and defended the state of his son's health.

"What if he had no lead in his pencil, if you get my meaning? I have to ask these questions what use would it be if any of the parties were as dry as a stone ditch? Firing blanks would not suit either party now would it? It's for the benefit of the first party as well as the second that I must conduct this arrangement in a proper manner. I've my reputation and envied position to consider. I'll be asking the second party the same questions or would you prefer that I didn't?" Louie looked from Breda to Greg and knew that he had won the day.

"Well, what do you think?" Greg queried some time later.

"It's not for me to disclose of my findings at this early stage. Now it is for you to tell me what kind of a dowry would satisfy you? Take into consideration that your son is not alone getting a wife but a housekeeper and a bearer of his children. That is if he can perform. There's nothing like a fine young broody girl to keep ones back warm at night and get up and do the chores early the next morning. When I've seen what the second party has on offer then I'll compare notes. I'll bid you good night and be away. I'll return within the week, God bless and thanks for the supper.

Curtain

185

Curtain opens in the home of Pat and Mary Slattery.

"*Hallo! Is anyone home? It's myself the matchmaker.*" Louie rapped
on the open half door of Pat Slattery's cottage. Inside all was silent.
'Where have they got to?' He was about to leave when Mary came
from up the field.
"*Good day to yourself. Is the man of the house about?*" Louie
removed his tall hat.
"*Who asking, he's down the long meadow?*" Mary studied the man in
the fancy garb standing before her.
"*I'm the matchmaker from Limerick. Louie Byrne at your service.*"
"*Oh! That fellow is it, hang on there and I'll give Pat a shout.*"
Without waiting for a reply she was off down the field hugging her
long skirt.
"*Pat, come up, you're wanted at the house.*" Louie looked down and
saw her standing on a dry stonewall waving and shouting.
"*What do you want?*" Pat stood washing his hands in the barrel
outside the door as he spoke.
"*He's the matchmaker Pat, came all the ways from Limerick, so he
has. I suppose you'll be wanting the sup of tae?*" Mary retreated into
the cottage and pulled the iron kettle over the coals.
"*A little refreshments would not go amiss. Have you by any chance
anything a little stronger than tae?*" The matchmaker sat down beside
the table.
"*Here try a drop of this.*" Pat removed a stone jug from the Welsh
dresser and presented it to Louie.
"*Much appreciated, is that apple pie that I smell?*"
"*It is indeed, would you like a slice?*" Mary removed a pie from the
Aga cooker and placing it on a large dish laid it on the table.
"*A fork if you please?*" Louie eyed the pie with watering lips.
No sooner had Mary presented him with the fork than he was delving
into the pie.
"*Wouldn't you like it on a plate?*" Pat asked.
"*No, this is grand, thanks.*" Picking up the jug he took a generous
swig.
Slowly the pie vanished from the dish without the matchmaker
speaking one word.

186

"Would you have a drop of baking soda, Mam? A touch of the wind if you must know." The matchmaker tapped his chest and belched.

"Sure I understand." Mary mixed a spoonful of bicarbonate of soda with hot water and handed it to Louie.

"Has he no shame, farting and belching all over the place?" grumbled Pat.

"Don't be so crude he didn't fart he brought up wind." Mary retorted.

"Whatever end it came from it's disgusting."

"Ah! That's much better, heartburn you know. Now regarding the match I must tell you that I have been in consultation with the first party. They're likely to strike a hard bargain."

"Did they mention the dowry at any stage?" Pat asked.

"Now, don't be hasty, that is for me to negotiate if you don't be minding." The matchmaker reminded them.

"Now what have you on offer?"

"Firstly there's our daughter Sara, well trained by Mary herself. As fine a cook as ever walked the land of Ireland. She's firm all round with a fine pair of child bearing hips, so she is, God bless her?" She is in her prime and broody and with strong arms and legs. She..."Pat was about to continue when the matchmaker stopped him.

"What I want to know is she familiar with housework and farm work. You know bread making, milking, potato planting and the like? Doesn't mind a drop of rain on her back? Further is she young enough for the transplant?" Louie studied his notes.

"Transplant! What does that mean?" Pat scratched his head.

"Transplant to new home, let me explain. Well! To tell you nothing but the truth I arranged a marriage over in Bruff. I regretted it ever since. It was widow woman who should have better sense. The new man she fancied was a big farmer with acres of land and a fine house. I tried to put her off the notion but she would have none of it. Nothing would please her until she got him into bed. Like an ould tree the transplant killed the roots. Perhaps it was the demands of the farmer, for his nuptial rights or overwork. Whatever was the cause she was found dead in his bed soon after the wedding? The family had the cheek to blame me. Wanted the fee back if you don't be minding."

"No problem with our Sara on that score, she's young and ready to be plucked. She'll be a Godsend to any bachelor seeking a companion

187

I can assure you. Sometimes I feared that she might want to become a nun. That was before she became broody like. What a waste of a good wife that would be? She being a fine homemaker and from the statute of her, a fine bearer of children. A woman to keep her husband warm and satisfied in bed and a bargain maker at any market or fair."
Mary added her happert worth.

"I see, I met the parents of the first party and they too told me in no uncertain terms that their son was more suited to the Priesthood."
Louie remembered meeting the first party.

"That's not all meself and Mary are getting on in years and Sara is our only offspring. God in his wisdom did not give us a son, so you see what I'm hinting at?"

"Go tell me more?" Louie sat up in his chair and was all ears.

"It's the farm, don't you see it will be hers together with the few pounds we have saved. Better still it is twice the size of the farm of the first party." Pat boasted.

"Does she make an apple pie as good as yours, Mary? Louie licked his lips.

"You liked the apple pie then? To tell you nothing but the truth it was Sara herself that made it." Mary proudly beamed.

" A girl of many talents, like her mother. Has she any other virtues that I don't know about?" The matchmaker was all ears, as they say.

"Go on Pat tell him about your brother's farm?" Mary interrupted.

"Ah! It's only a small hilly farm of about forty acres mostly mountain. Great for sheep but nothing else." Pat dismissed this mention.

"Are you telling me that she will inherit this farm as well?" Louie was hopping off his seat.

"Of course, my brother Jack is a confirmed bachelor."

"Two farms of land and a bank balance. I suppose it wouldn't do any harm if I walked the land; just to confirm what she's about to inherit?" The matchmaker rose from his chair and was half ways out of the house.

"If you think it might help with the negotiations then by all means. Pat show him round and when you're out I'll get a bite to eat ready."

"And all this is hers when you are both gone. What age did you say you are?" Louie eyed Pat up and down like a mortician.

"We're long livers to be sure but who knows when the good Lord might call one or both away."

188

" *True! No truer word said. There's as much call for the sheep as the lamb. No recent illness then, thanks God?*" Louie probed.

"*Not really, Mary had a bit of a chest infection but I rubbed it with the camphorated oil and she's fine now, thank God.*"

"*That's good, I see there's benefits to be had on both sides and I feel sure that a modest dowry in view of what you tell me will more than suffice.*" Louie rubbed his hands together.

"*That's good to know but keep most of this information under your hat. Wouldn't want the first party thinking that we wanted rid of our Sara?*"

"*I'll be the soul of discretion and I'll not mention the farms, of that be assured. I must say you have a fine farm of land so you have. Any man would give his eyeteeth for it, and then there's Sara. What a catch for any man.*" Louie had a far away look in his eyes as he spoke.

"*Come on then lets back to the house for the bit of grub.*" Pat and Louie sauntered up the meadow.

CURTAIN.

CURTAIN OPENS IN THE HOME OF PAT SLATTERY

Pat Slattery sat on the leaba suideachan (Settled Bed) a worried look on his face. He was dressed in his Sunday clothes and this meant that there was serious business about to be negotiated. Beside him the compulsory jug of poteen from which he would take the occasional sip. Wiping his mouth in the cuff of his coat he rose slowly and looked nervously towards the boreen.

"Mary! Whatever is keeping that ould git? Hoping no doubt to squeeze the last copper from us?" He shouted into the scullery.

"Will you be patient man and hould your whist. He'll come as sure as night follows day, so he will. Now lay off the hard stuff you need a clear head when bargaining with that sly ould fox." Mary! His long suffering wife came from the kitchen carrying a newly baked apple scone.

"I suppose that's for himself. Never put yourself out like that for me." Pat grumbled as she placed the scone on a plate.

"It's only a sweetener, now don't be jealous. Wasn't it you the one that I choose, couldn't get me between the sheets quick enough. Remember the kissing and the squeezing we done behind your fathers barn over there. God wasn't it great?" She teased.

"Don't take the Holy name in vain Mary, no luck will come of it." He looked up at her and half smiled as he noted her fresh cheeks and cheeky smile.

"I'll never forget them days Pat, so I won't. God! I was so happy." Putting her arms round him she planted a kiss on his cheek.

"Get off me woman. Behaving like one of them hussies. Have you no shame? We never did, whatever are you talking about? Look at me, my best suit covered in flour whatever will he be thinking?" Pat stuck his clay dudeen (pipe) in his gob and grumbled. "You were always a saucy one, Mary. I remember the first time that I approached your father, God rest his soul and told him of my intentions."

'Get out of here you young whelp that's for your elders to decide.'

"He stormed and with a kick up the backside sent me packing. Should have taken his advice and left it at that." Pat with his eyes half closed seemed to be lost in memories past.

190

"Weren't you the lucky one getting a fine girl like me? Here give me a smack for old times sake. She pursed her lips and held her arms open.
"Quiet now Pat, look who's in the boreen?" Mary glanced out from behind the lace curtains. Louie Byrne with his tall hat set at a jaunty angle and his shellaigh under his arm was approaching their door. Pat stood up to his full height and looked furtively out the half door keeping in the shadow so as not to be seen.
"He looks like he means serious business, he's got the tail coat on. Look at that top hat like a factory chimney? Taller than the Popes triple crown; I've no doubt. Now take my advice and don't be soft enough to give into his blarney. Talk the hind leg off a donkey would that one." Mary advised.
"Don't worry your pretty little head Mary, there's no cockles growing on this ould brain." Pat tapped his head with his pipe.
"God bless all here, I'm here to do the calling." Louie entered the kitchen and removed his hat before taking the holy water.
"It's yourself Louie and to be shure you're welcome. A sup of tae and a scone won't go amiss, I'm sure." Mary wiped her hands on her apron and genuflected before him. That beguiling smile and tasty apple tart would not soften Louie's heart.
"He's not a sagart (Priest) Mary. There's no need to make a fuss. Genuflecting before him indeed." Pat grumbled.
"Come over by the fire Louie, I've no doubt but you'll take the drop?" Pat picked up the jug and handed it to Louie.
"It's a good drop is it not? Tell me, where did it come from?" Louie lifted the jug he took more than a generous swig."
"A friend of the wife's over in Croom brought it." Pat was not about to disclose to the matchmaker where the poteen came from.
"I see! Ah well, God bless the distillers and may the excise man never cross his door." Again Louie put the jug to his lips.
"Got a bit of a thirst have we? We best leave the jug for now, Mary is about to wet the tae, aren't you Mary?" Discretions and Tactics had to be dictated when it came to Louie. He could be crabit at times.
"Sit yourself down Louie and don't be shy there's plenty more where that came from." Mary dusted the chair and temptingly placed an apple pie under Louie's nose.
"In the name of the father and of the Son and of the Holy Ghost... Bless us O Lord..." Pat began saying the grace before meals as Louie

191

removed a more than generous slice of the pie and stuffed it into his gob. He muttered an ejaculation that sounded like a prayer and hurriedly blessed himself before again helping himself to the pie.

"You like apple pie, Louie?" Mary beamed as he demolishing the pie.

"More like a pig in a trough." Whispered Pat.

"Are we ready to do the talking?" Pat asked some time later as Louie removed the last of the apple pie. Biting off an enormous piece he stuffed it into his mouth and mumbled something that Pat took for a, yes.

"That was the finest piece of apple pie that I ever ate, Thanks Mary. What do you think Pat?" He picked up the last of the crumbs from off the plate.

"I wouldn't know, I didn't see any of it. Mind you don't wipe the pattern off the plate, it's part of our wedding present." Sarcastically grumbled Pat as Louie scraped the plate clean.

"Did you say something Pat?" Louie reluctantly left the table and took his place beside the fire.

"He said nothing at all, just bladder all e. here have a sup. Now excuse us for a minute." Mary hurriedly handed the jug to Louie and followed her husband into the back bedroom.

"Pat whatever ails you, you ould goat? That's our salvation sitting out there, try and be mannerly." She chastised her husband.

"From the way you're fussing over him I was of the opinion that the Good Lord himself had entered our home. Bending the knee, dusting his chair and for good measure feeding him like a sow with a litter. One would think that you had the hots for him?"

"Ah come on Pat shure it's all show and for a good purpose. You know that I love only you." You're not jealous of the like of him, are you?" Mary hugged her husband and planted a cheeky kiss on his cheek.

Pat came from the bedroom carrying an old tin box followed by Mary. Carefully shielding it from Louie's view he opened it.

£200 we agreed, is that not so?" Pat kept his hand inside the box.

"Your memory is not doing you justice. You don't lose no time, now do you Pat?" Louie kept his hand out of Pat's reach; there would be no handshake until the deal was settled.

"Well! Do we have a deal or not?" Pat grumbled.

"Excuse me now Pat, you must be thinking of something else. Our agreement as I recollect of the persona grata, legally like was for the sum of £400 and the field above the fairy fort." Louie smiled beguilingly.

"You have a way with the big words. What was that you said?" Pat fidgeted inside the box.

"You're not that deaf Pat, Thank God? You know well what I said. Now stop all the shannagin and give me your hand." Louie insisted.

"Well seeing as she's a fine girl with grand child bearing hips I think that the first party is getting more than a bargain." Pat argued.

"Like best china is our Sara, always displayed on the top shelf, if you don't be minding." Mary added.

"To me they're all the same height, be they from Limerick, Kerry, Clare or Cork. The proof of the pudding is in the eating if I may remind you. Talking about your daughter? Until the bun is in the oven there is no need to crow. Did you not see the fine stature of the first party? Six feet plus and shoulders as broad as a ditch, God bless him. Like a well bred stallion and the best catch in the county. I'd be doing an injustice to his parents if I accepted anything less, so I would. Ruin my reputation so it would. Not minding you that your daughter is like a rose in bloom, God bless her." Louie feeling hurt proudly rose off his chair and blessed himself on mentioning the holy name.

"Come on now, tell you what... £200 and the field and I'll throw in my labour in building the cottage. How's that?" Pat bargained.

"A generous offer under different circumstances. No! The first party will take nothing less than £350 and the field plus your labour. Now give me your hand?" Louie spat on his hand and offered it to Pat.

"Take his hand Pat, it's the best we can expect." Mary advised.

"Very well then but I'll be expecting a generous Luck Penny." Pat spat on his hand and Louie took it. Pat reluctantly removed the dowry from the box and counted it into Louie's outstretched palm.

"There now, I hope that you are content. Robbing a poor ould couple of their life savings, may God forgive you?" grumbled Pat.

"Don't say that I was never more than generous?" Louie returned ten pounds as a Luck penny.

"Come on we may as well finish the jug after all you drank most of it." Pat now in a better frame of mind laughed.

The matchmaking had come to a satisfactory conclusion.

193

ACT TWO

*B*ack in the Slattery home.   ENTER Louie and the groom.

"*G*od bless the house, I've brought the second party in keeping with the legal and binding agreement." Louie entered the kitchen with the proposed groom in tow.

"You're welcome so you are. As you see my daughter is here already." Pat pointed out his daughter sitting under the casement.

"Sit yourself down there now beside our Sara. What's your name? Not too close now mind you." Pat warned the youth.

"My name is Greg." Stuttered the youth. Taking his cravat from round his neck he wiped the perspiration forming on his brow. He felt like a prisoner reluctantly assented to a life sentence. Sara looked up from under her eyelashes and with a beguiling smile made space for Greg.

"You didn't mention the farms to the first party, did you?" Pat nudged the matchmaker.

"What do you take me for? Of course I didn't." Louie whispered.

"We'll be having some refreshments I've no doubt." Louie stood before the fire and gave a cough signalling to his parched throat.

"Sure! Mary would you ever do the honours? You should have that throat of yours seen to." Pat sarcastically remarked. Mary ran into the scullery and returned carrying the obligatory jug of 'Poteen'.

"Good health Louie." Handing him the jug she genuflected before retreating to the side of her husband.

"Didn't I tell you not to do that, his head is big enough as it is." Pat whispered.

"Now here I have a paradigm of the agreement made between the second party, that's you Pat, and the first party, Gregory Duff senior, the grooms father. Who has signed the document witnessed in my presence? Without stultification and knowing that neither are parvenu or sceptical...'Louie took a long drink of Poteen and placed the jug on

194

the ground between his feet. Opening his coat he removed a hand written document, taking another long swig from the jug he began to speak.

"Isn't he the fine one with words, he looks for all the world like Robert Emmet?" Mary nudged Pat. Louie smiled from behind the document.

"What the F***** Hell is he saying? One would need to have a dictionary to understand what he's talking about. It's all double Dutch to me. Why can't he talk in plain English, gobbly gook...?

"Don't swear like that Pat, he knows what he's talking about."

"He's the only one who does. Talking from his arse, you mean."

"Quiet Pat wouldn't want to miss the big words, now would we?"

"What do you mean, miss them? You don't know any more than he does what they mean."

Clearing his throat the matchmaker continued...

"It is hereby noted that having received the agreed dowry that the young couple, Gregory junior and Sara here present can now do the walking out. Further let it be noted to all concerned that three months from this date they will both meet at the chapel gate for the nuptials. This agreement is witnessed by all parties whose names are circumscribed on this said agreement." Louie laid the document on the table and partook of a generous drink from the jug.

"Now Pat, this is a legal and binding document, so now we'll both sign it in the presence of each other and let the young ones witness it, how's that?" Louie took a fancy fountain pen from his inside pocket and unscrewed the top and shook it before offering it to Pat.

Pat looked down at the document. He had a hazy recollection of the perusal of the legal document but was not too good at the reading.

"Don't worry Pat, It's all legal and above board. I'll have a copy made for you so that both parties to the transaction have copies." Louie assured Pat on seeing him hesitate.

Drawing up a chair Pat sat down in front of the document and accepted the proffered pen and began to slowly sign his name.

"Jesus! Forgive me, what fine eloquence. I could be signing away my farm for all I know." Pat mused.

"Now Mary would you do the honours followed by the young couple?" Louie ignoring this remark nudged Pat off the chair.

"Now this is your section, Sara." Louie turned over the page and again read out the amendment to the agreement...

195

"My parents having delivered the agreed dowry to Gregory Duff, senior, I! Sara Slattery agree to a meeting at the Chapel gates within three months of the signing of this legal document with Gregory Duff junior to be married to same person in the said chapel. I acknowledge the names circumscribed on previous page one as due witnesses."

"Now me boy the same applies to you." He handed the pen to young Greg.

"There's no reneging now." Retrieving his pen he replaced it in his top pocket. *"The banns will be read from the pulpit this coming Sunday, no objections are there?"* Louie tucked his thumbs into his waistcoat and studied his captive audience.

"A good match and a very nice young couple. You did us proud Louie. Thank you!" Mary beamed.

The two men shook hands in triumph and downed the last of the 'poteen'.

Act Three *At the Chapel gates.*

" *Where* in God's name is she?" Gregory Duff, senior paced up and down outside the chapel gates in an agitated state.

"The bride will be late she's staying with her aunt up country. She'll be here, don't fear. Where may I ask is the matchmaker. That's what more important?" Pat Slattery demanded to know.

"I've not seen him hereabouts this last few months. Must be matchmaking up country." Another commented.

"Up country or not he should be here. He took my £350 dowry plus his own expenses easy like." Pat Slattery remarked as he ran his hand round his tight collar.

"Wha! What three hundred and fifty pounds? You mean two hundred pounds less the fifty pounds that he gave you as a luck penny. Are you trying to shame me in front of all the neighbours?" Gregory Duff senior insisted.

"On my mother's grave that's what I gave him." Insisted Pat.

"Your mothers grave? You wouldn't know the truth if it was staring you in the face." Greg came face to face with his adversary.

"You wouldn't be calling me a liar, now would you? You skuttering git." Pat stuck his finger into Greg's face.

"That's it, no more niceties. Come on, if it's a fight you want then I'm your man. Hold me coat Bredan." Greg removed his coat and passed it to his brother. Then like a Jack Russell terrier he challenged Pat. Both men squared up to each other like fighting cocks.

Soon a circle had formed round the combatants. The women screamed as both men punched and kicked, each trying to gain the advantage.

"Go on Pat show him what you're made of." Screamed Mary.

"Shut that gob of yours Mary Slattery or by God I'll shut it for you." Breda Duff came towards her and removed her shawl. Throwing it like a gauntlet on to the ground she attacked Mary. Soon both sides were locked in combat and a free for all was in process. Horses neighed and donkeys roared as the combatants fought each other under the bellies of the horses and over the graves of their loved ones.

"Stop it! Stop this at once, have you no respect for consecrated ground?" Father Tom Ryan, the Parish priest holding up the hem of his cassock came running down from the parochial house.

Soon the mêlée was called to order and ashamedly they stood before their pastor.

"Now what's all this about?" He demanded to know.

"It's the wedding father. There's no sign of Sara and the matchmaker is also missing." Pat informed him.

"Because they're late is that any reason for defiling sacred ground? Now is it?" Demanded the Priest.

"It's not alone that but Pat Slattery is making a liar out of me by claiming that I reneged on the dowry. I never did father, I swear." Gregory Duff senior looked contrite at the Priest.

"You did and here is the proof." Pat withdrew the document drawn up by the matchmaker from his pocket.

"Give that document here." Demanded the Priest. The Priest studied the document for some time.

"Did you read this before you signed it?" He held the document out towards Pat.

"You know that I cannot read very well, father. Louie read the document out to us before we signed it, isn't that so Mary?" Pat confessed.

"It's the truth Father, I heard it all with my own two ears, so I did." Mary verified her husband's statement.

"You were all duped, I'll read his name from the pulpit so I will. I doubt if we'll see him this day or any other day for that matter, but where can Sara be?"

"I told you father. The matchmaker obliged and took her up country to stay with one of her aunts. A holiday he claimed to prepare her for her nuptials. We were grateful and gave him his expenses. Louie will be here soon with our Sara, Have no fear on that score." Pat confirmed.

"We'll go up to the hill top, that way we will see them coming." Greg led the gathering away from the church.

"I'm not climbing any hill. Come on Mary we'll go inside and say a decade of the rosary." Pat suggested.

"Now no profanities Pat, not in the House of God" Mary followed her husband inside the church.

Final act...

In a cosy cottage far away...

"*Such beauty how could I resist you?*" *The matchmaker looked deep into Sara's eyes.*
"*I love you darling.*" *Sara with her arms tightly around his waist and with her pouting lips parted, her heart beating like that of a cornered hare, vowed her undying love for the matchmaker from Limerick.*
It meant nothing to her that the matchmaker was a man of sixty plus. That never entered her adolescent mind. To her Louie was as young as he felt.
Louie kissed her tenderly before sniffing the air.
"*I knew that you were the one for me when I saw you in my fathers cottage. You love me for myself, don't you?*"
"*Sara me darling what ever makes you say that? Course I do.*"
"*It's not the farms and the money in the bank, is it?*"
I'd marry you love if all you owned were the shoes on your feet. Still the farms will be a bonus. Now much as I'd love to hold you forever more, I think my apple pie is about ready and when you're at it wet the tae. Then there's the cow to be milked when you've finished that. You're a good girl Sara, so you are." *The matchmaker stretched himself.*
"*You're so wonderful with the words, love. I'll get your tae ready at once pet.*" *Sara jumped off his lap and genuflected before him.*
"*Will you come to the table for your supper or should I bring it to you, love?*" *Sara came into the sitting room and genuflected before Louie.*
"*Ah! You may as well bring it in here, I feel a bit tired. By the way the rain is coming on, best put a shawl over your head when you go milking. I wouldn't want you getting wet my precious, now would I?*"
"*That's what attracted me to you darling, you're so understanding. Showing such concern for my welfare.*" *Sara placed the tray on the*

199

matchmakers lap and again genuflected before leaving to carry out her chores.

"I know Sara Love, I know. Would you put another spoon of sugar in my tae? There's a good girl." He held the cup out to her.

"Sorry love I forgot." Sara again genuflected and apologised.

"That's alright love, but don't let it happen too often." The matchmaker relaxing in his sugan chair smiled that beguiling smile of his.

"We'll go and make the peace with your parents one of these days. Wouldn't what them thinking that we were ignoring them, now would we? The matchmaker suggested.

"They'll be thrilled when I tell them about our baby." Sara placed her hand on her stomach.

"Baby! Wha! Wha! What baby? Stuttered the matchmaker.

"We'll need to leave here and settle back into our farm." Sara smiled.

" Our farm! Indeed, indeed! Ah well another string to my bow?" Louie smiled as he sunk deeper into the sugan chair.

Experience of the past weeks had taught her that when Louie was in one of his capricious moods obedience was the better part of valour. Perhaps she had after all a doctrine of fatalism or was it wisest to take what comes? Had Louie not assured her that no better opportunity offered an assertion of her suppressed free will of the past? He had so much to offer in return for her affection. He could never ask too much of her. A fine young wife, two farms and a hefty bank balance what better dowry could a man wish for. Not forgetting a fine cook?

Louie had such a wonderful way with the words, how could any girl refuse him? Whatever it was that Sara Slattery thought; she at the tender age of sixteen years of age was now the wife and lover of the matchmaker from Limerick.

Trixy

The Secret
What is life, a sage I asked?
When never can the soul come back
From Astral worlds where calmly rests,
The souls of those who passed the test.
Question not the wise sage said,
The book of life remains unread.
Until such time when earths no more.
Universal secrets remain untold.
Louie Byrne©

Trixy followed her master along the old red path beside the river Shannon. She gave a comforting bark whenever she heard her litter call from inside the box that her master carried under his arm. Whenever her master looked down at her she would wag her tail delighted that he was so considerate to her children. Yet she wondered as to why he had to take them away from their comfortable home?

"There's a good dog." Her master reached down and patted her on the head. Whatever misgivings she had were dispersed by the kindness being show to her. She was assured that her master was taking good care of her litter. Up the stone steps went her master until he reached the big black bridge. Removing the box from under his arm he looked into the fast flowing river. Trixy began to worry and became agitated. She began to bark and approaching her master clung to his leg.

"Get down you stupid bitch." He raved as he kicked his faithful companion aside. Trixy felt the pain and let out a yelp but still returned to defend her children. She now knew that he had evil intent. She was determined to save her pups at any cost. Again she approached her master only this time wagging her tail and moaning. Perhaps he would have a change of heart? She crawled and cringed at his feet. She apologised with her eyes for any offence she or her children may have caused him.

He looked down at her licking his boots and noted her tearful eyes but there was no compassion. Laying the box on the parapet of the bridge he lifted his boot and gave her a kick to the side of her head. Dazed and astonished the little bitch again crawled to the feet of her master.

Wounded and in great despair she looked up at him and weakly wagged her tail. She lifted one paw contritely and looking up at him and again began to whine. There would be no reprieve as he lifted the box from the parapet and threw it into the fast flowing river.

Trixy made a vain effort to leave the scene and rescue her family but her master was too quick. Grabbing her by her collar he held her tight. Taking her leather lead from his pocket he beat her repeatedly. She began to panic fearing that she too was about to meet a watery grave. Her eyes grew wild with terror as the lead was finally secured in place. Bracing her legs she tried to resist but it was in vain.

"Behave yourself you stupid bitch." He challenged as he dragged her from the bridge. On returning home, he locked Trixy in the garage and retired to the house. She retreated to a far corner and began a sorrowful dirge of loneliness and utter despair. Whatever had she done wrong that her master was treating her so cruelly? Exhausted she fell into a fitful sleep only to be haunted by the ghosts of her lost children.

She awakened to hear the door being opened and saw in the dim light the outline of her mistress. Crouching on all fours she crawled to the open door and was soon on her way back to the bridge.

Without regard for her safety she raced down the long stone staircase leading to the Red Path and on to the riverbank. She ran along the water edge barking and calling to her lost children. There was no response all was silent. Then on the water edge she saw three little carcasses, tears again welled up in her sad eyes for these were the bodies of her children. Children that suckled her and frolicked and played with her no later than that morning were now dead. Taking one gently in her mouth she retreats to the meadow and laid it gently on the ground before returning for the other two. Beside the hedgerow she dug a grave with her sharp paws and places the bodies inside. Then with her strong nose she filled in the grave. She lay down on the lonely grave and mournfully sang a dirge for the loss of her babies.

Returning to the shoreline she continued her search for the others, perhaps they had survived? Reaching an upturned boat she crept under it to investigate. In a far corner she saw two more of her pups huddled together. She sniffed one, then the other before nudging them with her nose. There was no response, thinking that they too were dead she laid down beside them for the last goodbye. Gently she picked up one and took it to the meadow before returning for the second one. She licked them clean as she had done in life. After some time she thought that she detected a low moan and paused. Could her pups be alive, she thought? Snuggling closer to their cold bodies she drew them closer to the heat of her body and fell asleep. She awakened to find the pups trying to suckle her. Rolling to one side she exposed her tits to them. Greedily the hungry pups partook of the nourishing milk. When they had taken of their fill they rolled themselves into fluffy balls and fell asleep.

Trixy, now a happy mother went down the hedgerow sniffing as she went. Stopping she wagged her tail in excitement for she had discovered what she was searching for, before her lay the entrance to an abandoned Badger Set. 'This is the ideal place; away from prying eyes to raise what remained of my family', she thought. She had no intentions of returning them to her master after what he had done.

"Where does that bitch wander off to every day?" Her master grumbled as again he saw Trixy slink out the door.

The pups grew at a steady pace and she was finding it hard work to keep them concealed. On some of their walks her master would take her along the old red path. Although her pups were no more than a stones throw away she had trained them well, they would remain as quiet as Church mice.

Her master was fond of fishing and his favourite haunt was half way across the old metal bridge. He was a familiar figure to the train crew and as the old train trundled by they would exchange greetings.

One day as he fished the weather took a turn for the worst and he called it a day. Squally rain descended from the Clare hills as he walked along the track with his head into the wind. Suddenly his feet slipped from under him and he fell hitting his head on the rail knocking him unconscious. By late evening his wife began to worry. She looked out the window at the rain sweeping down from the hills.

"Trixy! Your master has not returned home and I am getting worried. I hope and pray that nothing has happened?" Trixy cocked her ear to one side sharing her mistresses concern. She began to bark and wag her tail and sniff the door a sure sigh that she wanted to go out.

"You don't want to go out in this weather, do you?" Again Trixy wagged her tail and barked.

203

"Away you go then old girl." Without a backward glance Trixy ran over the Black Bridge and on down the Red path. Under the railway bridge she ran and coming out the other side she stopped, what was that lying on the track near to the old metal bridge? Running as fast as her legs would carry her she did not stop until she came level with the still form. It was that of her master, she knew from instinct that something terrible must have happened to him. She nudged him and she licked his face but there was no response. She looked up the line and remembered that the Old Clare would soon be on its way from Limerick. It was doubtful if the driver would see him in time through the squall, she had to do something. Instinct once again told her that her master's life was in imminent danger.

She thought of her two remaining children hidden in the meadow. She had to take a chance on their being discovered and drowned. Putting all her doubts and concern aside she raced back along the railway line. Reaching the meadow she began to bark. Two heads appeared from inside the hedgerow. She saw their long tails wagging and again began to bark only this time with some urgency. They looked at each other and knew that something must be wrong. Racing through the long grass they came up beside her. She explained the situation to them and the risk involved should they be detected. They could remain hidden in the meadow or join their mother in her rescue bid.

There would be no reluctance on their part for duty and defence of their master was inbred into them.

Trixy, explained her plan and the three left the meadow. She told them to stand in the centre of the track below the old stone bridge. On hearing the whistle of the train they were to start barking and jumping up and down. They must stop that train even though they may have to sacrifice their young lives in the process, she warned. She would return to the spot where her master lay and stand by him. If they were still alive after stopping the train they were to run down the line barking and encouraging the train crew to follow them.

"Good luck children." Trixy licked each one and with tears in her eyes ran off down the track. Pausing she looked back at her two children and thought 'Will I ever see them alive again?'

The two young collies sat side by side on the track with their ears cocked. In the distance they heard the familiar sound of the Old Clare as it trundled along the track. Then the train was within their view,

204

they looked in fear and trepidation as the monster approached them belching out fire and smoke. Rising they began barking in unison and jumping up and down.

The fireman was the first to see the young collies on the track.

"What the blazes are they up to, they'll get themselves killed?"

"Blow the horn that will frighten them away." Instructed the driver. The fireman continued blowing the horn as the two young collies pursued on their suicidal mission.

"What's wrong with you two? Get off the track." The driver shouted from the cab window. Taking no notice of his warning the dogs continued to approach the fast moving train.

"You had best stop Jack, there must be some rational explanation for such conduct?" The fireman challenged.

With a screech of brakes the little train stopped within feet of the collies.

Both men left the train intent on shooing the dogs off the track. The dogs waited until they were within feet of them before taking off down the track. Stopping after a few yards they again began to bark.

"What's wrong with that pair of fools?" Jack asked as they retreated up the track. The dogs on seeing them returning to the train followed them and in an agitated state began to bark and run round in rings.

"Get off the line you stupid mutts." The driver began throwing stones at the dogs but although some of the stones hit them they would not be deterred. The cat and mouse game continued for some time.

"Do you know Jack I believe they want us to follow them, something must have happened up the line?" The fireman looked at the two excited collies.

"I was coming to the same conclusion myself. Come on you two show us what is wrong?" The driver called.

Meantime the local residents having heard the train hooter blowing over and over again were of the opinion that something must be amiss. They gathered on the old stone bridge overlooking the line and were surprised to see the abandoned train. Going down on to the line they followed the outline of the crew as they heading towards the metal bridge.

"Jesus help us! Is that not a body on the line and look that's Trixy beside it?" Trixy seeing her two children leading the rescue party

205

rose to her full height and began to bark and wag her tail. Her two remaining children had done her proud.

"You can relax now old girl, you saved your master's life." All hands were intent on congratulating the mother. Trixy went and sat beside her two children, they were the hero's of the day.

"Sorry Trixy in the excitement, we forgot about the two young collies." Jack laughed.

A stretcher was procured and Trixy together with her two children followed it to the waiting ambulance.

"Sorry Trixy you cannot come, go on home now. You done your master proud." The nurse spoke to the dogs.

Her master on recovery was sent home to recuperate.

The train crew came one evening to visit the patient and were surprised to see him sitting up in bed reading the 'Limerick Leader.'

"Glad to see you making a speedy recovery." Jack held out his hand in greeting.

"Thanks to you two, I owe you my life."

"You owe us nothing, had it not been for the three collies who knows what the outcome might have been?"

"I was reading the story in the paper, it would seem that it was my Trixy assisted by two young collies that saved my life. I would like to find their owner and thank him. Do you know him?"

"Sorry! We never saw them before or since."

"If they are strays and you see them again bring them here. I'll see you right. There is a comfortable home waiting for them."

Trixy cocked her head to one side and wagged her tail. Letting out a little bark of appreciation she was out the door heading for the meadow. No doubt bringing the good news to her two young heroes.

THE ROSE OF MOONCOIN

'How sweet 'tis to roam by the sunny Suir stream;
And to hear the doves coo 'neath the morning sun beam.
Where the thrush and the robin their sweet notes entwine,
On the banks of the Suir that flows down to Mooncoin:'

Mooncoin! A village in County Kilkenny of little significance apart from a love affair that was due to failure from the start...

Walter Murphy was born into the Roman Catholic faith in the spring of 1790 in the village of Rathkiernan in the County Kilkenny. Walter followed in his fathers' footsteps when he opened his own school in the village of Mooncoin. His love of music and poetry became a byword throughout the county. As his pupils had little to give by the way of payment in fees for the upkeep of the school it was in danger of closing. Relief came when the school was taken over by the local parish and Walter was retained as its teacher.

Walter was not too happy with the way his teaching methods were being questioned by the governors. A small man with a fiery temper he soon brought the matter to the fore and this led to his dismissal.

During his exile, Walter spent his days walking along the bank of the river Suir composing music and poetry. On one of his meanderings he came across the newly appointed vicar to the local village of Polerone by the name of Wills. The vicar had a beautiful daughter named Molly, not yet out of her teens whereas Walter was now nearly sixty years of age. Molly too had a love of music and poetry and would spend many hours sitting with Walter on the banks of the Suir composing music and poetry with him. The inevitable happened when one evening she told him that she had fallen in love with him. Although Walter was forty years her senior he was flattered. Their love affair however was to become a shameful scandal but not because of the age difference. Molly was a Protestant and Walter was a Roman Catholic. The parish Priest would not participate in their wedding nor would her father, the vicar. Elizabeth made it clear to her father that she was now a woman. She could make up her own mind and would marry her Walter.

207

"Marry that old man? You'll do no such thing. Don't you realise that he is a Papist?" Her father warned.

Walter was approached by the parish Priest and told that should he wish to marry Molly Wills then she would have to take instruction in the Roman Catholic faith and be accepted into the church. Walter, a man with a mind of his own told the priest that they would not be dictated to by him or the church.

"If you will not marry us in Church then we will go and live together for we love each other." Walter told the shocked Priest.

As their affair was causing a scandal in the village it was decided that the best solution was to separate them.

How they were to achieve this was the problem. The Roman Catholic Bishop would not allow his parish Priest to hold a discussion on the matter with the vicar and visa versa.

The vicar worried for his daughters' reputation decided to take matters into his own hands. One dark night he had his daughter kidnapped and bundled into a coach. She was driven at speed to the port and taken on board a ship bound for London.

Walter now found himself alone with his sorrow. He took to walking along the banks of the Suir singing laments to his lost love.

"Walter! Snap out of it, she's gone and there's nothing that you can do about it." His friends would try and comfort him. They watched as his health deteriorated and his clothing became ragged.

"Oh! Molly, dearest Molly my fond heart is breaking. Why did they part us? Why destroy our love?" Looking out over the waters of the Suir he'd call to his Molly now far away...

"I'll always love you darling and cherish the days we spent, you and me Molly by the banks of the Suir that flows down to Mooncoin." It was on one of his walks that he composed and dedicated the beautiful song

'The Rose Of Mooncoin'

to their lost love..

Walter died from a broken heart 'On the banks of the Suir that flows down to Mooncoin' still pining for his beloved 'Molly'

Shane

In the townland of Dunlewy near the poison glens in the county of Donegal there lived a boy named Shane.
He spent many hours exploring the glens and mountains surrounding his isolated home. When the weather permitted he would travel deep into the poison glens and pretend that he was a Gaelic chieftain fighting the forces of Elizabeth the first of England. He would stalk the wild deer and try to capture one of the many rabbits that lived in the glen. They took little, if any notice of his childhood pranks. They would watch in amusement his every movement and play along with him.
Shane was an only child and longed for a companion to while away the long winter days and short summers. A younger brother or sister would be welcome. What his heart ached for more than anything else was a dog. He fancied a great big Irish wolfhound. Then he could be like the great Cuchulainn defending the pass at the yellow ford. He pestered his father day in and day out for a dog until his father forbid him ever mentioning one again. When his father failed to respond to his pleas, he turned to his mother, Monica. If only she would use her influence and persuade his father to let him have a dog. He promised that he would love and care for him and her too. He would teach him to be obedient to all the rules and be his constant companion. He would teach him to run and fetch the washing when it blew from his mothers washing line. He would teach him to herd his fathers' sheep. This he claimed would be a boom to his family who were now getting on in years. Little did he know how much his mother heart ached knowing how lonely her son was.
There was little enough money to feed them from the produce of the rocky land. Shane could not understand the heartache he was causing his parents by his insistent requests for a dog. If they could afford it then by all means they would get him a dog.
They had far greater need for a donkey to carry the heavy creels of turf from the bog. Barefooted and with hardly enough to sustain them they had to carry the backbreaking creels down the mountainside on their backs. If they had the money then their preference would be for a donkey.

Shane could see no prospects of ever getting a dog. 'Where would a dog come from out here in the wilds?' He thought.

Perhaps the fairies living in the rocks by upper lake Nacung would come to his assistance. After all did not his parents often tell him of the power of the fairies?

'That is it, I'll take myself off to the lake of Nacung and have a word with them personally.' He spoke aloud to himself.

Shane slept little that night and was relieved when he heard the big red rooster crowing. His mother came from the bedroom and began to rake life into the fire. He rose from his bed and washed his face. Opening the door he looked across that the top of the great mountain. It looked a long distance away. Early snow sat atop the mountain making it look like the Christmas cake his mother had made. How long would it take him to climb the mountain, cross to the lake and return back home? He tried to calculate the distance in his young mind. What lay beyond the mountain he wondered? His father often spoke of the fairies living in the old fort by the lakeside.

"Shane come and sit down, your stirabout is getting cold." He was brought back to reality by his mothers' voice calling to him.

"I'm off on a long journey this morning, Mother. Can I take my scone with me please?" Shane informed her.

"You can of course, not going too far are we?" His mother was used to his childhood fantasies and took little notice of his wanderings.

"You cannot come mother, this is personal." He informed her.

"Very well then but wrap up well. The weather is not too kind at this time of the year." His mother warned him.

Shane rolled his piece of cake in a linen cloth and tied it to a stick. Taking the holy water he placed the bundle on his back and opened the half door.

"I'm going now mother, I'll be back in time for supper." He closed the door and wandered off down the old boreen.

She came to the half door and looked after her son. How often she thought had he gone on his many childhood adventures? If only he could have a sister or brother. Then that was the will of Almighty God. She heaved a sigh and closed the door as a wayward hen made to perch on the half door.

The mountain of Errigal seemed so near as he reached the mountain path. The gorse and heather was now burnt brown and he could hear *the grouse clacking beneath the heather. The mountain looked like a huge bald giant with a beard. Yet no matter how many miles he travelled the mountain seemed as elusive as ever. Finally he found himself climbing, he had finally set foot on the mountain itself. He looked back at his cottage, it seemed so very far away compared with the distance of the mountain from his home. Tired from the long climb he sat down on a rock. Opening the cloth he ate a portion of the scone. A robin came and stood before him with its head cocked to one side. Picking off a portion of the scone he threw it to the bird. With a tweet of a thank you the robin hopped across and ate it.*

There was a slight flurry of snow in the air but that was not unusual in the hills of Donegal. He must hurry for although the weather was fair it could change for the worst without warning. Rising to his feet he looked up at the foreboding height of the mountain, would he ever be able to climb to the top and beyond? With a sigh and a prayer on his lips he struggled on. The hard granite stones bit deep into his bared feet.

Rounding a bend he saw that the road now descended down the mountain. He would not have to climb to the top. He saw the blue water of the lake shimmering in the distance. He quickened his steps and listened as the loose rocks cascaded down the mountain and crashed deep into the valley floor below. The big rooks were annoyed by the intrusion and swaked their protest as they flew along the sky - line. The track petered out and he found that he was now on a mossy bank leading to the lake. The cool moss comforted his bare feet. A fairy fort stood between him and the lake.

Then he remembered that his mother put out food every Halloween for the fairies. Well it was not Halloween but he felt sure that the fairies would be just as hungry in September as November. Cautiously he crept towards the fort, he was sure that he heard noises coming from within. Blessing himself he crept within a few feet of the circle. He felt the blood racing through his heart and stopped, all was now silent.

Blessing himself once again he reached out and placed a portion of the cake underneath a hawthorn bush. Then he called on the fairy king to come and talk with him. There was no response, he again called, nothing but the music of the gentle babbling waters.

'How silly of me, I should have made an appointment.' He thought.

211

"Fairy King! If the weather is good to morrow and my mother lets me, I'd like to come and discuss a matter of some urgency with you." Rising to his feet he left the fort.

Next morning the weather was fine and Shane once again packed his lunch and made the long tiresome journey over the mountain to the lake. His feet were still sore from the previous journey but it would be all worth it should the fairy king be waiting to meet him.

"Now what should I say to him? He is a king and not used to little boys. I know what I'll say, I'll say"... Shane scratched his head.

"Fairy King! Please can I have a dog and I'll never come near to you again," He thought for a while.

"No! That will not do, it is not polite." Deep in thought he came nearer and nearer the lake.

On the shore he saw the fairy fort and stood for some time looking deep into it. The piece of scone that he had left the day before was gone. It was not as frightening to look at as he imagined but the fairy King was not waiting. Surely he would not disappoint him.

He was warned to keep away from the fairies. They would steal him and keep him in their fairy fort forever more. If he wanted to meet the fairy king then he would have to approach his rath (fort). He sat down on a rock and ate some more of the cake.

"I hope that the Sidhe Ri (Fairy King) has not forgotten our appointment?" He thought as he watched a hawk hover above his head.

At the lakeside he sat down once again and began to think before he entered the fort.

"Fairy King! Would you please grant me just one wish? I do not want a crock of gold, just a dog, please." This he thought would be enough to get his message across.

Entering the fort he placed the piece of cake under the bush and sitting on a rock waited.

Finally as he was about to leave a little man in a caipean dearg (Red Cap) came out and sat beside him on the rock.

"What are you doing, sitting here on my rock?" The little man looked across at him.

"Sorry Sir! I'm... I'm waiting to meet the fairy King." Shane fell off the end of the rock in fright.

"Waiting for me is it you were?" The little man laughed.

212

"Yes Sir! That is if you are the fairy king." Shane brushed his trousers and returned to his seat next to the man.

"Well! Get on with it, what do you want?"

"I want! I want!" Shane stammered forgetting in the excitement what he had called for.

"You want what? Come on out with it. You mortals are always looking for something for nothing."

"Oh no! It's not like that, I need a dog." Shane forgot what he had rehearsed to say.

"A dog! A real dog? Well I never heard the likes. What kind of dog would you like?" The fairy king removed his caipean dearg and scratched his head.

"Well a sheep dog if you have one please."

"We don't keep dogs, but I'm sure that we can find you one. Nothing is impossible to the Tuatam-De-Dannan you know."

"Oh thank you! Thank you, I'll bring you a whole cake to morrow." Shane jumped off his seat in his excitement.

"Don't bring any more cake, it only makes me fat. Now away home and let me look for a dog for you. A sheep dog you said? Before you go, tell me do your parents know about this request?"

"Oh! They know alright, it's just that they have no money to buy me one."

"I see! Very well then, away you go before it gets dark." Shane returned home to his parents in great fettle.

"Mother do you know that I am going to get a dog? A big sheep dog." He excitedly told her. Then he remembered about the Irish wolfhound but it did not matter.

"A sheep dog is it, and where is this dog coming from?"

"The fairy King is out now looking for one for me."

"What's all the excitement about now?" His father entered the cottage.

"I'm getting a dog, father and I'm going to call him Caesar."

"Where is he getting the dog from Monica, we have no money?"

"Tell your father about your dog." Monica returned to baking a scone.

"From the fairies father, and they don't want any more scone, it makes them too fat." Shane informed them.

213

Days went into weeks and Shane kept a daily vigil at the rock but there was no sign of the fairy or the dog.

Shane began to pine for the promised dog and as the autumn gave way to winter he was forced to curtail his visits to the rock.

"It will soon be Christmas Monica, I wish that I could get Shane that dog" His father slumped into the sugan chair.

"Don't fret about it, God is good he will do something, you'll see."

*On Christmas Eve Shane packed a lunch and travelled across the Errigal Mountain, again in search of the fairy and his elusive dog. The skies darkened and a bitter cold wind was blowing by the time the reached the gap leading down the mountain. A snowstorm swept down the mountain obliterating the path, there was no way forward and no way back. He would have to seek shelter. Finding a cave he crawled inside and listened to the crying wind. Stories he had heard round the turf fire of the **Bean- Ó-Sídhe** frightened him.*

All day the storm raged and by nightfall the cold was eating into his bones. He was frightened and alone on the mountaintop.

His parents in the meantime were out in the hills searching for their lost son.

"Shane! Shane where are you?" They called as they struggled across the mountain. They too were forced to return to their home. Shanes mother removed the Connail Mhor from its linen cloth and kissing it she placed it in the window. He would see the blessed candle in the window from wherever he was and be assured that they were coming for him. All night long they sat within their cottage waiting for the storm to abate before they would once again venture out as far as the lake.

In the meantime Shane sat huddled inside the cave shivering. 'Would he ever see his home again'? He wondered what had happened to the fairy and his dog. Perhaps they too were caught in the storm and it was entirely his fault. Rolling into a tight ball within the confines of the cave he soon succumbed to sleep.

He was awakened next morning by noises echoing through the mountain. He went to the mouth of the cave and looked across at the valley. It was covered in a thick blanket of white snow. Nobody would find him now; he heard the church bell ringing calling the people to mass this Christmas morning to celebrate the birth of the Infant Jesus.

Above the clanging of the bell he heard or thought he heard a dog barking. No! It was just the wind; he pulled his ragged clothing closer about him. He heard it over and over again it was a dog barking. Somewhere out there in the mountains was his dog looking for him. He ran to the mouth of the cave and began shouting.

"Caesar, come here Caesar." He shouted above the storm.

Into the cave dashed the biggest sheep dog that he had ever laid eyes on. The dog ran into his arms and knocking him over began to lick his face. This was the finest sheep dog that ever roamed the hills of Donegal.

"I had a lot of searching to do before I found you, will he do?" The fairy King entered the cave, removed his caipean dearg and shook the snow from it.

"Oh Caesar! Caesar what a wonderful Christmas present you are." Shane was too engrossed with the dog to hear what the fairy said.

"I said is he what you wanted?" The fairy repeated.

"He is beautiful, you are so good to me, thanks." Shane jumped to his feet and ran to thank the fairy.

"There is no need for that. Tell me do you have any scone left?" Shane shared what scone he had with the fairy. The fairy lit a comfortable fire where Shane soon settled down with his dog and succumbed to sleep.

"Wake up Shane, your parents are here they have come to take you and your dog home." The fairy king gently shook Shane.

The dog began to bark as he heard voices and ran from the shelter.

"Shane! Shane where are you?" There were now several voices calling.

"What is it?" Shane rubbed the sleep from his eyes.

"It's your parents coming for you." The fairy king told him.

Finally over the ridge of the mountain came the dog leading the rescue party.

"Oh Shane! Shane, thank God that you are safe." His mother ran into the shelter and embraced her son.

"I'm alright, the fairy king saved me and brought me a dog." Shane looked into the shelter and pointed to the ledge where the fairy was sitting.

"Who saved you, son? There is nobody here but you. Where did that sheep dog come from?" His father asked

215

Shane looked all around the mountaintop and into the shelter but the fairy had gone.

He was soon wrapped up in warm clothing and on his way down the mountain with his dog.

Shane paused and looked behind at the mountaintop. On a high peak stood the fairy waving his caipeen dearg.

Shane took off his cap and waved back, and then he called on his parents to wave too.

They looked at the bleak peak of Errigal mountain but could see nothing. They looked at each other, and then smiled in that knowing way and removing their caps waved them.

"Merry Christmas Sidhe Ri." They greeted. Their voices echoing round the valleys and mountains of Donegal.

"This is the finest Christmas present we ever had love, Merry Christmas."

"And to you Love."

Shane's parents kissed and embraced as they heard Shane calling to his sheep dog deep in the poisoned glen.

From the pen of the same Author
* Dare you ripple my Pond
* Tears on my Pillow
* No light in the Window
*Autobiographic Trilogy
Cry the cursed Land
Felons of our Land
Lest we Forget
Tandy
Rainbows seldom touch the Ground
Ancient stories of Ireland
In the glow of the turf fire
The adventures of Peaches
Little book of doggerel stories and Verse
Limericks' forgotten History
The Auction
The sweet silver Bells
The fox is on the Hill
Last throw of the Dice
etc: